BRAIN ACADEMY
MATHS
Teacher's Book

Louise Moore, Sally Harbour
and Richard Cooper

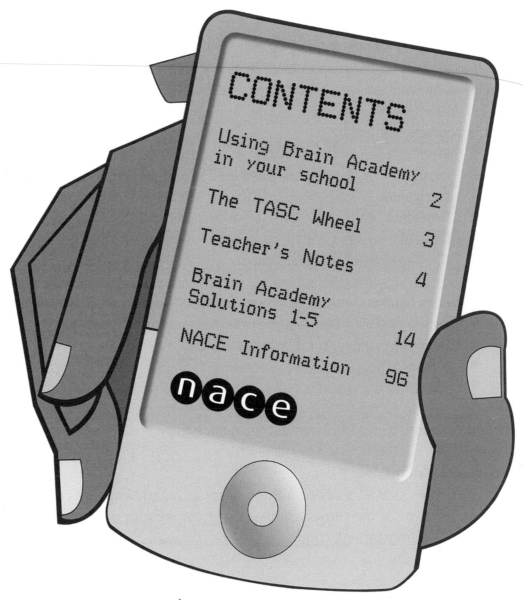

CONTENTS

nace

RISING ★ STARS

Using Brain Academy in your school

Brain Academy is a series of five books designed to provide a wealth of activities and investigations for your able, gifted and talented children. The activities are set in rich contexts that will enliven and enrich children's experience of Mathematics.

A step–by–step approach to using Brain Academy

1) Read the story on the left hand page with your group or class. This sets the context for the Mission File.

2) Complete the Training Mission at the bottom of the left hand page with your class or group. Using a whiteboard or flipchart will help here. This introduces the mathematical concepts to be covered in this mission.

3) Children can complete Mission 1 on their own, using the experience of the Training Mission plus the Think Tank hints and the further support on pages 44–47.

4) Bring the group back together to share their experiences and then either set the Da Vinci Files as an investigation to be done at home or out of class or alternatively, work through the investigation together.

Using the TASC Problem Solving Wheel

Thinking Actively in a Social Context: TASC is a well-researched universal thinking skills framework developed by Belle Wallace, President of NACE.

TASC empowers learners to:

- Work independently yet within an inclusive school policy
- Develop skills of research, investigation and problem-solving that can be used across the curriculum
- Develop a positive sense of self as an active learner
- Demonstrate their abilities using the full range of multiple intelligences
- Develop skills of self-assessment

TASC provides teachers with a framework for:

- Lesson planning that systematically develops pupils' thinking
- Effective planning for differentiation and extension
- A holistic approach to incorporating the multiple intelligences
- Assessing the processes of pupils' learning

To find out more about TASC contact www.nace.co.uk

Developing Brain Academy

If you are interested in developing Brain Academy by trialling, reviewing or writing more materials to cover other areas of the curriculum please see our website www.risingstars-uk.com or email benbarton@risingstars-uk.com.

The TASC wheel

All children can learn to be better thinkers.

They just need to practise the <u>strategies</u> of expert thinkers!

Learn from experience

Children need to think about their learning.
Talking about what they have learned extends mental maps and connects ideas.

Gather/organise

Ask the children to gather together what they already know. This can be oral or jotted down quickly in a flow–chart or mind map.
This process gathers information stored in the memory and brings it into the working memory ready for action.

Communicate

Children need to share their thinking, sharing is a celebration!
Telling someone else clarifies the process of problem–solving.

Identify

Ask the children to explain the task in their own words.
Ask them to highlight the key words.
This helps to clarify the task and to focus on the key elements.

TASC

Evaluate

Let the children decide if they were successful.
Encourage re–thinking and revisions.
Emphasise that 'mistakes' are good learning points.
Encourage self–appraisal and self–assessment.

Generate

Even if there is a conventional 'right answer' encourage the children to think of other possible solutions.
Always encourage creative thinking and develop the self–confidence to explore possibilities.

Implement

The children can work orally or with quick sketches, flowcharts or mindmaps.
Maximum thinking and talking!
Minimum necessary recording!

Decide

Let the children decide on the strategy they will use.
This encourages decision–making and self–confidence.
This prioritises action!

TASC: Thinking Actively in a Social Context © Belle Wallace 2004

MISSION FILE 1: TEACHER'S NOTES

MISSION FILE	MATHEMATICAL CONTENT	Teacher's Notes
1:1 1:18	100 square Counting in 2s, 3s, 4s (1:1) Counting in 5s, 6s, 7s (1:18) Multiples (1:18) Pattern finding Prediction and testing (1:18)	A copy of a 100 square is needed for 1:18 and it is useful for reference in 1:1, too. Encourage students to use different colours to distinguish between the 2s and 3s, etc, when colouring/marking on the number squares. This way they will not get confused when looking for patterns. In 1:18 the word 'multiples' is used. Check that children are happy with the equivalence of a number's multiples and its times table, i.e., the multiples of 2 are 2, 4, 6, 8... which is the two times table.
1:2 1:4 1:8	Addition (1:4) Subtraction (1:4) Multiplication (1:4) Division (1:4) Odd and even numbers (1:8) Pattern finding (1:2, 1:8) Sorting into groups (1:8)	These three missions give nice number work practice but with a purpose! The sums involved lead to pattern spotting. 1:4 is a good follow-on to 1:2, using subtraction, multiplication and division as well as addition. 1:8 is an excellent extension of 1:2; results in 1:2 could be referred to when working on 1:8 to reinforce the patterns observed in this mission. Check the children are happy about the meaning of 'odd' and 'even' numbers before starting 1:8 and that they remember to look at the last digit to decide if a number is odd or even.
1:12	Addition Differences Odd numbers Triangle 'Magic Square'	This is a great puzzle style mission that all children will enjoy. Trial and error (and perserverance) is what is needed here. Could be used in class as a final Friday afternoon exercise after a tiring week, or as a fun homework activity.
1:3 1:13	Combinations (1:3) Permutations (1:13) Pattern finding Prediction and testing	In 1:13 we are <u>not</u> interested in order, just which combinations of sweets or combinations of boys and girls, so if 'GO' is recorded in TM 1), there is no need to record 'OG' as this is the same combination of sweets. In 1:13 we <u>are</u> interested in the order of the flowers, so we record both the arrangements 'RY' and 'YR' in TM 1).
1:5 1:14	Addition Subtraction Money Combinations (1:5)	These Mission Files provide excellent exercises on money. Mission File 1:5 is great for exploring the value and equivalences of coins. When listing the combinations in the Da Vinci Files, use a systematic approach and remember to make exchanges: two 10ps could be replaced by 20p and one 10p by two 5ps. The activities in Mission File 1:14 are very good for covering the topics of using money and giving change.
1:6 1:10	Drawing and naming 2-D shapes Polygons (especially irregular ones) Right-angles (1:10) 3-D shapes (1:10)	These are great missions for children that get too used to seeing regular polygons and therefore do not recognise an irregular hexagon as a hexagon. Use squared paper for drawing the shapes. Children may find it useful to make or to be provided with templates of the shapes given in 1:6, M1, so they can physically move them around. Check the term 'right-angle' is fully understood in 1:10. It may be useful to use the corner of a piece of paper with the children to clarify the term.

MISSION FILE	MATHEMATICAL CONTENT	Teacher's Notes
1:16	Sharing / division Even numbers Counting down in 4s More than	It would be useful to start this mission off with a discussion of an example, so that children can confidently tackle the questions. a) Share 12 DVDs between TWO boxes so that one box has FOUR more DVDs than the other. b) What if you had to share them between THREE boxes, so that each box contains two more than the box before it? Solution to be discussed with the children: a) put FOUR DVDs in one box and NONE in the other, so that at this stage one box clearly has FOUR more than the other. Now share the remaining EIGHT DVDs equally between the TWO boxes, so one box will have 4 + 4 = 8 and the other has 4. b) put NONE, TWO and FOUR DVDs in the boxes, so that each box clearly has TWO more than the last box. Share the remaining SIX equally between the boxes to give TWO in each, so we will have 2, 4 and 6 DVDs in the boxes.
1:9	Mid-points between two numbers (1:9) Halving Doubling (1:11)	Both of these missions involve halving, but in 1:9 we are halving the difference between two numbers. Children will find it useful to have number line portions to work with, so for TM 1) could simply draw: 10 11 12 13 14 15 16 17 18 19 20 mid-point Encourage them to mark the mid-point on the line. N.B., the mid-point of two numbers (a, b) will always be $\dfrac{a + b}{2}$
1:7 1:17	Fractions (1:7) Interpreting charts (1:7) Drawing a pictogram (1:7) Equivalent fractions (1:17) Addition of fractions (1:17)	Mission File 1:7 combines handling data with straight-forward fraction work using half, quarter and three-quarters of four. For Mission File 1:17, the children must be happy dealing with halves, quarters and tenths, be able to add fractions with the same denominator, such as $\dfrac{3}{10} + \dfrac{2}{10}$ and recognise $\dfrac{5}{10} = \dfrac{1}{2}, \dfrac{1}{2} = \dfrac{2}{4}$
1:15	Grid references Compass directions (N, S, E, W)	This is a fun spatial mission. Use 1cm squared paper and get the children to make eight copies of the map shown in M1 to use for M1 and Da Vinci questions. To check answers to M1 3) and 4) and Da Vinci Files, get the children to swap with a partner and see if the routes work.

MISSION FILE 2: TEACHER'S NOTES

MISSION FILE	MATHEMATICAL CONTENT	Teacher's Notes
2:1 2:3	Combinations Money Addition	2:1 Combinations of 1p, 2p, 5p } 2:3 is a good consolidation 2:3 Combinations of 5p, 10p, 20p, 50p } of 2:1 or possible homework Combinations of 1p, 2p, 5p } following 2:1 in class. Encourage a systematic approach to listing the combinations, so that all possibilities are obtained. Where there are many possibilities, as in 2:3 Da Vinci, it is a good idea to draw up a table with the values of the coins and to use trial and error to see which combinations of coins give the required amount. Consider the exchanges of coins that could take place if you have a combination involving two1ps. This could be replaced by a single 2p to yield a different combination.
2:8	Combinations Time Money	Most children would enjoy the variety of Mission File 2:8, with its basic combination work and straightforward time and money calculations. Advise the children to record their M1 answers in systematic tables for easy reference when working on the Da Vinci Files, where there are many possible scores.
2:5 2:11	Combinations Multiplication Addition	Mission File 2:11 is a good homework or extension activity following work on Mission File 2:5. In 2:5 consider how many police officers there are if there is one dog, how many for two dogs and so on. For every extra dog there will be two less officers. Similarly, in 2:11 consider the more complex exchanges between Zogs and Zugs (and Zigs).
2:6 2:14 2:15	Combinations Addition Multiplication (2:15) Interpreting charts (2:14)	In 2:6 and 2:15 we are interested in totals, so permutations of the arrows/sacks do not need to be listed. For example, if 5, 3, 1 is given for a total score of 9 in 2:6 TM 2), 3, 5, 1 should not be listed. In 2:15 we are concerned with different sums. You may wish to discuss the two sums 2 + 3 and 3 + 2. Encourage children at this level to give both permutations, but be understanding to those who are reluctant!
2:4 2:7 2:15	Combinations Pattern finding Prediction (2:4 and 2:18)	For 2:4 and 2:7 it is a good idea to regularly check that children are getting the right answers as they work through these missions. This will ensure that the correct patterns are identified. In 2:18 a systematic method is vital to list the many possible combinations and to spot the pattern. It may be useful to go through TM 1) and 2), demonstrating the layout of the solutions after the children have attempted these questions, to ensure they continue the mission in an effective way.
2:10 2:13	Addition Making 10 / Number bonds Decision making (2:13)	These are two nice problem solving missions that are fun to work on. The questions will generally be solved by trial and improvement, although 2:10 M1 needs a more methodical approach.
2:2 2:9	Permutations Symmetry (2:2)	These two mission are all about permutations where order is important! In 2:2 TM 1), RBBR is one permutation of the beads and BRRB is another. Help children to understand that they are the same combination of the four beads given.
2:12	Division Factors Polygons (square / hexagon) Vertex Even numbers Addition	This mission combines number with shape. The children may need to reminded of the term 'vertex' so check their understanding of the vocabulary used here and that they are clear on the number of vertices on a square and a hexagon. The divisions involved in M1 may provide a discussion point. 1) $(24 - 4) \div 4$ 2) $24 \div 4$ 3) $(24 - 6) \div 6$ 4) $24 \div 6$

MISSION FILE	MATHEMATICAL CONTENT	Teacher's Notes
2:16	Combinations Addition	It would be useful to start this mission with some discussion of the problem, to ensure everybody understands it clearly. Every bird has its own unique set of crest feathers, so if a particular Tri bird has three green feathers, no other Tri bird could have green feathers and neither could any of the other types of bird. Encourage the use of a table to record the results, starting with the maximum number of Uni birds and then exchanging two Uni birds for a Bi and so on.
2:17	Shape, circle drawing Regions / area Greatest / least Money	Advise the children to use a pair of compasses and to draw the rings as simple circles of the same size. Accurate drawing is important if all the regions/areas are to be found. Encourage the children to think about the orientation of the circles in order to maximise the number of overlaps. See the diagrams in the solutions for this mission. A great activity for a Friday afternoon!

MISSION FILE	MATHEMATICAL CONTENT	Teacher's Notes
3:4	Shape Rectangles Triangles	It would be useful to introduce this mission by considering a similar problem with the children first. For example: How many squares can you count? 1 x 1 squares = 9. 2 x 2 squares = 4 3 x 3 squares = 1 Total = 14 Count the triangles carefully in M1 and watch out for trapeziums!
3:13	Using operations (+, −, x, ÷)	This mission is based on a calculator. In order to do this exercise you could let the children use a calculator or choose not to use one if you want them to practice their number skills. Two-digit numbers will need to be used in M1 and Da Vinci Files: for example, to make 14, calculate 32 ÷ 3 x 1.
3:1 3:6 3:8 3:9 3:12 3:14 3:17	Problem solving Halving (3:1) Distance (3:9) Fractions (3:12) Even numbers and prime numbers (3:14) Time (3:17) Weight (3:6)	These missions will test the children's problem solving skills and can usually be answered in two ways, by trial and error or algebraically. Both methods are not always shown in the solutions for every question. If trial and error is used, it must be done in a systematic way (see solutions for 3:9 and 3:14). If attempting to use algebra, children may first write a general statement in words and may then require help to proceed.
3:5 3:10 3:15	Permutations Even numbers (3:5) Multiples (3:15) Maximum (3:15) Factors (3:15)	These missions are about arrangements where order is important, so in Mission File 3:10 the firemen are in a line and the arrangement HBB is different to BHB. In Mission File 3:15, where many permutations of the digits are possible, rather than simply listing the arrangements systematically, the children could consider how the number of permutations come about. For example: For the first digit there are four choices: 1, 2, 3 or 4. Once this digit is chosen there are three remaining numbers to choose from for the second digit, two numbers for the third and the remaining number is the fourth digit, so one choice. This means there will be 4 x 3 x 2 x 1 = 24 permutations.
3:16 3:18	Combinations Money (3:16) Problem solving (3:16)	In Mission File 3:16, trial and error can be used in M1 as prices are all multiples of 50p. The solutions are easy to reason out: Cheesy spud + cup of tea = £3.50 } So cheesy spud is £1.50 Sponge pudding + cup of tea = £2.00 } more than sponge pudding. Since sponge pudding + cheesy spud = £4.50, we know cheesy spud must be £3.00 and sponge pudding is £1.00. Therefore, a cup of tea is 50p. Also, see algebraic method in solutions. In Mission File 3:18, use a systematic listing of the combinations. You may assume the vans in TM are identical, so if the two pairs A,B and C,D are listed, then C,D and A,B is not another possibility. But in M1 and the Da Vinci Files Nick, Rob and Phil are not triplets!

MISSION FILE	MATHEMATICAL CONTENT	Teacher's Notes
3:3	Using multiples or times tables Money	For this mission, encourage children to use systematic trial and error. Draw up a table, start with 0 families of 3. Is it possible to make up the remaining number (24 in this case) with families of 4? Yes, 6 x 4 = 24. Now try the same thing with 1 family of 3. No, it is not possible to make 21 with 4s, and so on.
3:2	Counting in 4s, 5s, 7s, and 12s Multiples Square numbers	The mission provides a fun way for children to make lists of square numbers and their relevant times tables and to scan these for the correct solutions, rather than just using guess work. In M1, it may be useful to talk about the best way to go about these problems. If you are counting in sevens and there are three pieces left over, it means the number you are looking for is a multiple of seven plus three more.
3:7	Logic problems Addition	Most children will love this mission. To record the information given in either TM or M1, use a table (see solutions) and tick or cross appropriate boxes. As soon as you get a tick in a particular row and column, you can fill the remain boxes in that row and column with crosses.

MISSION FILE	MATHEMATICAL CONTENT	Teacher's Notes
4:1 4:3	Ratio Multiples Combinations (4:3)	In these missions, ingredients (4:1) or cans and bottles (4:3) must be kept in the same ratio. In Mission File 4:3, M1 can be solved by trial and error (in a systematic way). In 1) try one lot of six and see if the remainder (46 – 6 = 40) can be made with the four's. Since 10 x 4 = 40, we have a solution. There are three solutions for this question and it is worth challenging the children to find all three.
4:2 4:9	Problem solving Logic problems (4:2)	Children will have great fun with these missions. In Mission File 4:2, the key to solving these problems is to remember to take the individuals themselves into account. They can be solved algebraically or by trial and error. Setting up the equations if choosing to solve algebraically is not always easy. For TM it would be: Total no. of firefighters = $(x + 1) + x + 1 = 4(x - 1) + x$, where x = the no. of women one more man than women / women / Sam / excluding Pam no. of men / women In Mission File 4:9 work systematically and remember there always needs to be somebody to row back for the others.
4:11 4:17	Addition Subtraction Using code (4:11) Calculator (4:17)	These missions provide lots of practice in number work. As an extension to Mission File 4:11, discuss why the remaining letters of the code cannot be found (not enough information, no obvious pattern in the letters and numbers given). Children could design their own codes. Mission File 4:17 is based on a calculator. In order to do this exercise you may choose to let the children use a calculator or choose not to use one if you want them to practise their number skills. One and five can easily be made as 4 – 3 = 1 and 2 + 3 = 5, so the numbers one to ten can all be made.
4:8 4:14 4:16	Multiples	These mission give excellent times table practice. In Mission Files 4:14 and 4:16 you are looking for lowest common multiples. In 4:16 it is the LCM of the times they start work. In Mission File 4:8 you are looking for multiples that have been adjusted to give the relevant remainder. In TM, instead of listing 3, 6, 9... you list 5, 8, 11... and look for the first number in common with the list: 10, 17, 24...

MISSION FILE	MATHEMATICAL CONTENT	Teacher's Notes
4:12	Sequences and pattern finding Addition	These missions are all about sequences. For Mission File 4:12 the sequences are called arithmetic progressions. In general, if you have a sequence of numbers with a common difference (d) then the sum of n terms if the first term is 'a' would be: $$\frac{n}{2}\,[2a + (n-1)\,d]$$ For example in TM 1) the sum of five terms is $\frac{5}{2}[2 \times 2 + 4 \times 2] = 30$ Although children are unlikely to come up with this formula, they may well be using it without realising, especially if they pair up the numbers in the sum, e.g., in TM 2) each pair adds up to 22, so the sum is $\frac{10}{2} \times 22 = 110$. $$2 + 4 + 6 + 8 + 10 + 12 + 14 + 16 + 18 + 20$$
4:7 4:10 4:15	Combinations and arrangements Odd and even numbers (4:7) Multiples (4:7) Prime numbers (4:7) Time (4:7)	Mission File 4:7 is an exercise with nice variety. Remind the children what prime numbers are and that number one is not prime. If you have got the time and the space it is nice to demonstrate the first questions of TM in 4:10 and 4:15. Don't worry if you don't have a circular table for 4:10, just arrange the chairs in a circle and label them A-E. Encourage the children to work in a systematic way when listing combinations. In the 'handshake problem' in 4:15 we generate the triangular numbers (1), 3, 6, 10, 15, 21...
4:4 4:5	Shapes Area (4:4) Perimeter	These missions are about fencing off land. Square paper would be useful. Both missions could be used as a class work and homework combination. Remind the children how to find area and perimeter as they often confuse these terms and concepts.
4:6 4:13	Shape and space Distance Speed and time (4:13)	These missions give good practice in travelling around square grids. Centimetre squared paper would be useful here. The missions could be used as a class work and homework combination. Encourage the children to mark the routes on copies of the grids and use arrows, otherwise some routes will look identical.
4:18	Shapes Patterns	Use multi-link cubes to help you get to grips with this mission. This is the well known 'painted cube problem'. There is a great pattern to the number cubes with different numbers of painted faces, so refer to the solutions and encourage the children to think about where their answers are actually coming from.

MISSION FILE 5: TEACHER'S NOTES

MISSION FILE	MATHEMATICAL CONTENT	Teacher's Notes
5:7 5:9	Addition Sequences (5:7) Consecutive numbers (5:9)	In Mission File 5:7 encourage the children to look for patterns in the numbers they are adding. $(0+)\ 1 + 2 + 3 + 4 + 5 + 6 + 7 + 8 + 9 = (1 + 9) + (2 + 8) + (3 + 7) + (4 + 6) + 5 = 45$. If you add the digits of pages 10, 11, 12, 13, 14, 15, 16, 17, 18 and 19 you would have ten number 1s and $(0+)\ 1 + 2 + 3 + 4 + 5 + 6 + 7 + 8 + 9$. So the sum for this set of pages is $(10 \times 1) + 45$. Similarly, for pages 20-29 the sum for these pages is $(10 \times 2) + 45$. The pattern starts repeating at 100 pages. For Mission File 5:9, draw the children's attention to Huxley's Think Tank. These relationships and thinking about the sizes of the numbers will help them. Also, see TM solutions for a useful rule to check if a number can be made by a specified number of consecutive numbers.
5:10	Multiplication	This is a fun investigative task. Remind the children that anything multiplied by zero will give zero.
5:3 5:12	Ratio Time and speed (5:12)	In the recipes in Mission 5:3 the quantities are based on the first ingredient given in each list. Encourage the use of grams in TM and suggest giving the answers in terms of jugs in M1. Remember, however much mixture is being made, the ingredients must be in the same ratio. For Mission File 5:12, get the children to work out how many laps Prince Barrington and Echo will have done for every one lap that Mrs Tiggles and James Bond complete. Drawing clock faces may help, as will marking the slower pairs' position after every lap completed by the Price and Echo.
5:14 5:15	Conversion of time (5:14) Conversion of Metric ↔ Imperial (5:15)	In Mission File 5:14 there are many conversions between seconds, minutes, hours and days. Remind the children how many days there are in each month: a calendar may be useful for those who get in a muddle! The conversion factors between Metric and Imperial units is given in Mission File 5:15, but the children will need to remember that 1000ml = 1 litre, 1000g = 1kg, 12 inches = 1 foot, etc.
5:6 5:16 5:17 5:18	Fractions Time (5:16, 5:17, 5:18) Money (5:16)	These missions make fractions fun! There is a lot of adding (so equivalent fractions will need to be found) and some multiplying by whole numbers. In Mission File 5:16, work backwards through the information given. In TM, 16 minutes corresponds to 1/4 of the time at that stage, therefore 3/4 would be 3 x 16 = 48 minutes, so the bus journey took 48 minutes. For Mission File 5:18 we know that from 1.30pm to 1.50pm, (3/4 – 5/8) 1/8 of the journey was completed, so 1/8 = 20 minutes. In Mission File 5:17, if children are unhappy with 1.25 agents being freed, discuss the idea that this is an average rate per day, or that they have dug one quarter of the way to the next agent.
5:2 5:8 5:11	Shape Cost (5:2) Patterns (5:8, 5:11) Addition Square numbers (5:8, 5:11)	Look at sequences and patterns in these missions, otherwise they (especially 5:13) will take forever! In Mission File 5:1 it is important for the children to realise that the General keeps going around and around the circle until <u>all</u> the agents have been questioned, so that his last questioning is of the agent in the blue hat. If he questions every nth agent, then he always starts with the nth person from blue in a clockwise direction. For Mission File 5:13 look at the symmetry of a palindromic number. Give some examples and discuss which two-digit/three-digit numbers will display that symmetry. Encourage a systematic listing.

MISSION FILE	MATHEMATICAL CONTENT	Teacher's Notes
5:4	Capacity	In TM you have to make the numbers 1–10 using 1, 3, 6 and addition or subtraction only. Some children may actually like to try doing the activity with water, so if you have the appropriate size containers this could be a fun classroom exercise!
5:5	Logic problems	In TM the solutions can be found without too much trouble, but in M1 there is so much information that a table to record the data is vital. Remember, once a box has been allocated to a person all the other boxes in the same column can be eliminated.

Square dance

TM

1)

13	14	15
23	24	25
33	34	35

2)

76	77	78	79
86	87		
96	97	98	99

3)

5		7	8
	16		18
15	16		28

4)

42		44		46
	53		55	
62			65	66

M1

1)

1	2	3	4
5	6	7	8
9	10	11	12
13	14	15	16

2)

1	2	3	4
5	6	7	8
9	10	11	12
13	14	15	16

3)

1	2	3	4
5	6	7	8
9	10	11	12
13	14	15	16

4)

1	2	3	4
5	6	7	8
9	10	11	12
13	14	15	16

Da Vinci files

2s

1	2	3	4	5
6	7	8	9	10
11	12	13	14	15
16	17	18	19	20
21	22	23	24	25

3s

1	2	3	4	5
6	7	8	9	10
11	12	13	14	15
16	17	18	19	20
21	22	23	24	25

4s

1	2	3	4	5
6	7	8	9	10
11	12	13	14	15
16	17	18	19	20
21	22	23	24	25

5s

1	2	3	4	5
6	7	8	9	10
11	12	13	14	15
16	17	18	19	20
21	22	23	24	25

6s

1	2	3	4	5
6	7	8	9	10
11	12	13	14	15
16	17	18	19	20
21	22	23	24	25

All the patterns so far are diagonal or vertical lines. If you investigate in larger squares other patterns will emerge as well.

It's a tall story

TM

1) 0+3
1+2
2+1
3+0

2) 0+4
1+3
2+2
3+1
4+0

3) 0+5
1+4
2+3
3+2
4+1
5+0

M1

1) 0+6
1+5
2+4
3+3
4+2
5+1
6+0

2) 0+7
1+6
2+5
3+4
4+3
5+2
6+1
7+0

3) Check children's work

Da Vinci files

Number	3	4	5	6	7	8
Number of sums in the number story	4	5	6	7	8	9

1) The number of sums in the story is always one more than the number.
2) One less than twelve is eleven, so answer = 11

3) 0+11
1+10
2+9
3+8
4+7   which has 12 sums
5+6
6+5
7+4
8+3
9+2
10+1
11+0

4) Check children's work

It's in the bag!

TM

1) GG, GO, OO (3 ways)
2) GGG, GGO, GOO, OOO   (4 ways)
3) GGGG, GGGO, GGOO, GOOO, OOOO (5 ways)
4) GGGGG, GGGGO, GGGOO, GGOOO, GOOOO, OOOOO   (6 ways)

M1

1)

Number of sweets	2	3	4	5
Number of ways	3	4	5	6

2) There is one more way than the number of sweets.
3) Ten sweets have eleven ways.

GGGGGGGGGG, GGGGGGGGGO, GGGGGGGGOO, GGGGGGGOOO,
GGGGGGOOOO, GGGGGOOOOO, GGGGOOOOOO, GGGOOOOOOO,
GGOOOOOOOO, GOOOOOOOOO, OOOOOOOOOO

Da Vinci files

BBB, BBG, BGG, GGG

A memory mystery

TM

1) 4 + <u>21</u> = 25   25 − 21 = <u>4</u>
    25 − <u>21</u> = 4   <u>25</u> − 4 = 21
2) They all use the same three numbers.
3) 8 + 14 = 22   14 + 8 = 22   22 − 8 = 14   22 − 14 = 8

M1

1) 18 + 32 = 50   32 + 18 = 50   50 - 32 = 18   50 - 18 = 32
2) 35 + 65 = 100   65 + 35 = 100   100 - 35 = 65   100 - 65 = 35
3) Check children's work
4) 4 x 2 = <u>8</u>   2 x <u>4</u> = 8
   8 ÷ 4 = <u>2</u>   <u>8</u> ÷ 2 = 4
5) They all use the same three numbers.

Da Vinci files

1) 3 x 2 = 6   2 x 3 = 6   6 ÷ 2 = 3   6 ÷ 3 = 2
2) 5 x 4 = 20   4 x 5 = 20   20 ÷ 5 = 4   20 ÷ 4 = 5
3) Check children's answers

MISSION FILE 1:5
Mrs Tiggles's money-hunt!

TM

1) 1p + 1p = 2p, 2p + 2p = 4p, 5p + 5p = 10p, 10p + 10p = 20p,
   20p + 20p = 40p, 50p + 50p = 100p or £1, £1 + £1 = £2,
   £2 + £2 = £4
2) 1p + 2p = 3p, 5p + 10p = 15p, 10p + 20p = 30p,
   50p + £1 = £1.50, £1 + £2 = £3

M1

1) a) 10p   b) 50p   c) 20p   d) 20p
2) 50p + 5p + 5p   or   20p + 20p + 20p

Da Vinci files

50p + 50p + 10p + 10p + 5p + 5p + 5p + 5p + 5p + 5p
50p + 20p + 20p + 20p + 10p + 10p + 5p + 5p + 5p + 5p
50p + 20p + 20p + 10p + 10p + 10p + 10p + 10p + 5p + 5p
50p + 20p + 10p + 10p + 10p + 10p + 10p + 10p + 10p + 10p
20p + 20p + 20p + 20p + 20p + 20p + 10p + 10p + 5p + 5p
20p + 20p + 20p + 20p + 20p + 10p + 10p + 10p + 10p + 10p

TM

1) a) hexagon   b) octagon   c) pentagon
2) Check children's work for 2 hexagons, 2 pentagons, 2 octogons.

M1

(Children's answers may differ)

1) a)

triangle

b)

quadrilateral
(square)

c)

pentagon

d)

hexagon

e)

heptagon

f)

octagon

g)

nonagon

h)

decagon

Da Vinci files

(Children's answers may differ)

11 sides

12 sides

13 sides

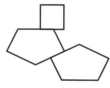

14 sides

15 sides

Save our seaside!

TM

1) One piece of rubbish is ◖

2) a) 2 pieces   b) 1 piece   c) 3 pieces

M1

1) a) 5 crisp packets
   b) 8 rusty cans, 4 more than quantity of ice-cream wrappers
   c) 17 pieces of rubbish altogether

2) a) 24 rusty cans
   b) 3 more crisp packets than ice-cream wrappers
   c) 51 pieces of rubbish altogether

Da Vinci files

1) Crisp packets 25; rusty cans 40; ice-cream wrappers 20
2) Check children's work

An odd day's work

TM

1) Odd: 43, 7, 99, 1, 21, 35, 21
   Even: 82, 42, 64, 50, 78, 24, 78
2) Check children's answers for 10 odd and 10 even numbers.

M1

1) a) 8   b) 12   c) 20   All the answers are even.
2) Adding two odd numbers always gives an even number answer.
3) a) 6   b) 14   c) 10   All the answers are even.
4) Adding two even numbers gives an even answer.
5) An odd number added to an even number gives an odd number answer.

Da Vinci files

Odd answers: 68 + 121, 123 + 442, 56 + 27, 35 + 126
Even answers: 345 + 27, 652 + 666, 75 + 63, 90 + 24
Check sums that children have added.

MISSION FILE 1:9
A whole ladder trouble!

TM

1) 15
2) 9
3) 45

M1

1) a) 75
   b) 100
   c) 70
2) a) 43
   b) 23
   c) 29
3) 0 and 12, 5 and 7, 4 and 8
Check children's work for other solutions.

Da Vinci files

1) 20
2) 40
3) 90

It's a right-tangle

TM

1) 4
2) Square, rectangle, triangle (right angled!), other irregular polygons may be drawn.
3) Circle, regular polygons (other than square), triangles (not right angled)

For 2) and 3) children may also give other answers.

M1

1) Examples that could be listed are books, furniture and door.
2) 4 on each face x 6 faces = 24 right angles
3) 4 on each face x 6 faces = 24 right angles
4) The number of right angles stays the same whatever the size of the cuboid.

Da Vinci files

1) 4 right angles on a face, 5 faces outside and 5 faces inside = 4 x 10 = 40
2) 4 right angles on each face, 5 faces outside, 5 faces inside and 2 faces on the lid (front and back) = 4 x 12 = 48 right angles
+ 4 right angles formed by the open top
48 + 4 = 52 right angles

Double trouble

TM

1) 80 guests at 6pm, needing 50 parking spaces.
2) 30 pizzas, 46 pies, 64 sausages, 100 drinks

M1

1)

Say	1	2	3	4	5	6	7	8	9	10	11	12	13	14	15	16	17	18	19
Mean	2	4	6	8	10	12	14	16	18	20	22	24	26	28	30	32	34	36	38

Say	20	21	22	23	24	25	26	27	28	29	30
Mean	40	42	44	46	48	50	52	54	56	58	60

2) a) They need 2 cars (Agent A says double what they need).
    b) Dr Hood thinks they need 8 cars (he thinks 4 is half the number needed).

3) a) Agent A brought 5 (He thought Dr Hood was saying double the number).
    b) They need 20 (10 is half of 20 which was the code Dr Hood used).

Da Vinci files

1) double 20 = 40
    double 40 = 80
    double 80 = 160   (3 doubles)
2) double 50 = 100
    double 100 = 200
    double 200 = 400
    double 400 = 800
    double 800 = 1600   (5 doubles)
3) Any number from 25 – 249
4) Any number from 7 – 62

MISSION FILE 1:12

Line up!

TM

1) and 2)   6, 4, 2, 4, 6   and   6, 4, 6, 4, 2

1) 4 6 3   2) 2 1 4
    5   7   7   3
    2 8 1   8 5 6

Check children's work as there are other answers.

3)   1   4)   2
     3   6   1   3
   5 2 4   4 5 6

Da Vinci files

One solution is:
6 4 5
4 5 6
5 6 4

Other solutions may be possible.

MISSION FILE 1:13
Flower power!

TM

1) RR, RY, YR, YY
2) RRR, RRY, RYR, YRR, RYY, YRY, YYR, YYY

M1

1) RR   2 ways
2) RRR, RBR, BRB, BBB   4 ways
3 a) There are half as many answers than in TM.
   b) They are different because you can't choose the colour for the last pot
      – it has to be the same as the first one.
4) RRRR, RRBR, RBRR, RBBR, BRRB, BBRB, BRBB, BBBB

Da Vinci files

1)

Number of pots	2	3	4
Number of arrangements	2	4	8

2) The number of arrangements keeps doubling.
3) Double 8 is 16, so 16 arrangements for 5 pots.
RRRRR, RRRBR, RRBRR, RBRRR, RBBRR, RBRBR, RRBBR, RBBBR,
BRRRB, BRRBB, BRBRB, BBRRB, BBBRB, BBRBB, BRBBB, BBBBB

Sandy's secret admirer is Buster Crimes!

MISSION FILE 1:14
Shop 'til you drop

TM

1) a) 90p   b) 50p + 50p = £1, so change is £1 − 90p = 10p
2) a) £6.50 + £2.50 = £9
   b) Change is £10 − £9 = £1

M1

1) 50p + 50p = £1
2) Tin of cat food and packet of dog treats.
3) Tin of cat food and carton of milk.
4) Carton of milk and dog treats   OR   Fish food and tin of cat food

Da Vinci files

1) £2 each
2) Answers will vary – check children's work.

TM

1) A3, E1, E3
2) A2, B2, C2, D2, E2
3) D3

M1

1) A3
2) F3
3) and 4) Check children's work

Da Vinci files

1) Answers will vary but a possible solution is:
Start in B4. Move up one, then right one. Go down four, right one, up one, right one, up three, right one, down three, right two, down one into H1.

2) a) Up 3, right 5   OR   right 5, up 3 (could use compass directions)
b) Answers may vary but a possible answer is:
East 7, North 3, West 2   (might not be compass directions)
c) Answers may vary but a possible answer is:
South 1, East 5, North 4   (might not be compass directions)

TM

1) 4 and 10 ducks
2) 1 and 9 hats (8 more), 2 and 8 (6 more), 3 and 7 (4 more), 4 and 6 (2 more)

M1

1) Put 2 in the second box and 4 in the third. Used 6 books and have 9 left. Share these equally between the three boxes – get three each.
Box 1 – 3 books; Box 2 – 5 books; Box 3 – 7 books

2) Put 3 in the second pot, 6 in the third and 9 in the fourth. Used 18 pens and have 6 left. Share these equally between the three pots – get 2 each.

Pot 1 – 2 pens; Pot 2 – 5 pens; Pot 3 – 8 pens; Pot 4 – 11 pens

3) Each car contains 1 more – 5, 6, 7 lampshades
Each car contains 2 more – 4, 6, 8 lampshades
Each car contains 3 more – 3, 6, 9 lampshades
Each car contains 4 more – 2, 6, 10 lampshades
Each car contains 5 more – 1, 6, 11 lampshades

Not enough lampshades to go any higher

Da Vinci files

Working backwards, 17, 13, 9, 5, 1.
1) The youngest got one.
2) 17 + 13 + 9 + 5 + 1 = 45
3) 5 children

MISSION FILE 1:17
Fraction in-action

TM

1) If the pieces are not the same size then they are not halves.
2) a)

 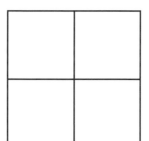 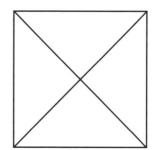

b) You could measure the pieces or you could weigh them.

M1

1) a) $\frac{5}{10}$ b) $\frac{1}{2}$ Other answers are possible.

2) a) 2   b) $\frac{3}{4}$

Da Vinci files

1) $\frac{5}{10} + \frac{1}{10} = \frac{6}{10}$ so there are $\frac{4}{10}$ left

2) $\frac{1}{10}$ each

3) Check children's work

MISSION FILE 1:18
End games

TM

1) They are all even numbers – they end with 2, 4, 6, 8, 0
2) They end in 5 or 0
3) They end in 0

M1

1) a) ... an even number.
   b) ... 5 or 0
   c) ... 0
2) a) The last two digits will be an even number and then a zero.
   b) The last two digits are a 50 or 00.
   c) The last two digits are 00.

Da Vinci files

1) 132, 400, 60, 550, 700, 248, 150, 30, 140, 170
2) 60, 400, 550, 700, 95, 150, 30, 140, 170, 125
3) 60, 400, 550, 700, 150, 30, 140, 170
4) 60, 400, 700, 140
5) 400, 550, 700, 150

Fund-raising for fire-engines!

TM

Work through these with coins. Pick 10 coins and work out the amount. If there is too much money change a large value coin for a smaller value coin. If there isn't enough change a smaller value coin for a higher value. Repeat until the correct amount is reached.

1)   10 x 2p   or   2 x 5p, 2 x 2p and 6 x 1p
2)   4 x 5p, 4 x 2p and 2 x 1p   or   5 x 5p and 5 x 1p
3)   10 x 2p and 10 x 1p   or 2 x 5p, 2 x 2p and 16 x 1p

(There may be other solutions – check the children's work)

M1

1) and 2)

$$1p + 1p + 1p + 1p + 1p + 1p = 6p$$
$$2p + 1p + 1p + 1p + 1p = 6p$$
$$2p + 2p + 1p + 1p = 6p$$ 5 different ways to pay
$$2p + 2p + 2p = 6p$$
$$5p + 1p = 6p$$

3) $1p + 1p + 1p + 1p + 1p + 1p + 1p + 1p = 8p$
$$2p + 1p + 1p + 1p + 1p + 1p + 1p = 8p$$
$$2p + 2p + 1p + 1p + 1p + 1p = 8p$$
$$2p + 2p + 2p + 1p + 1p = 8p$$ 7 different ways to pay
$$2p + 2p + 2p + 2p = 8p$$
$$5p + 2p + 1p = 8p$$
$$5p + 1p + 1p + 1p = 8p$$

4) $1p + 1p + 1p + 1p + 1p + 1p + 1p + 1p + 1p + 1p = 10p$
$$2p + 1p + 1p + 1p + 1p + 1p + 1p + 1p + 1p = 10p$$
$$2p + 2p + 1p + 1p + 1p + 1p + 1p + 1p = 10p$$
$$2p + 2p + 2p + 1p + 1p + 1p + 1p = 10p$$
$$2p + 2p + 2p + 2p + 1p + 1p = 10p$$ 10 different ways to pay
$$2p + 2p + 2p + 2p + 2p = 10p$$
$$5p + 2p + 2p + 1p = 10p$$
$$5p + 2p + 1p + 1p + 1p = 10p$$
$$5p + 1p + 1p + 1p + 1p + 1p = 10p$$
$$5p + 5p = 10p$$

Da Vinci files

Only coins that could be handed over where 2p would be change and not return of the money given is two 5ps, so the cream cake cost 8p.

2 x 5p change 1p → cake cost 9p   5p + 2p change 1p → cake cost 6p
2 x 2p change 1p → cake cost 3p

(3 possible answers)

MISSION FILE 2:2
A gem of a challenge!

TM

1) RRBB, RBRB, RBBR, BRRB, BRBR, BBRR (6 solutions)
2) RBBR and BRRB are symmetrical

M1

1) BRRRR, RBRRR, RRBRR, RRRBR, RRRRB (5 ways)
2) 1 symmetrical design   RRBRR
3) 3 symmetrical designs   RBBBBR,   BRBBRB,   BBRRBB
4) 3 symmetrical designs   BBRRRBB,   BRBRBRB,   RBBRBBR

Da Vinci files

6 symmetrical designs
GBRRBG, GRBBRG, RGBBGR, RBGGBR, BRGGRB, BGRRGB

MISSION FILE 2:3
A close call!

TM

1) One (20p)
2) 4 x 5p
3) 10p and 10p   10p, 5p and 5p   2 other ways

M1

1a)   20p + 10p   20p + 5p + 5p   10p + 10p + 10p   10p + 10p + 5p + 5p

        10p + 5p + 5p + 5p + 5p

1b)   5p + 5p + 5p + 5p + 5p + 5p   (6 ways)

2a)   20p + 20p   20p + 10p + 10p   20p + 10p + 5p + 5p

        20p + 5p + 5p + 5p + 5p   10p + 10p + 10p + 10p   10p + 10p + 10p + 5p + 5p

        10p + 10p + 5p + 5p + 5p + 5p   10p + 5p + 5p + 5p + 5p + 5p + 5p

2b)   5p + 5p + 5p + 5p + 5p + 5p + 5p + 5p   (9 ways)

Da Vinci files

(29 ways)

1p	2p	5p
20	0	0
18	1	0
16	2	0
15	0	1
14	3	0
13	1	1
12	4	0
11	2	1
10	5	0
10	0	2
9	2	1
8	6	0
8	1	2
7	4	1
6	7	0
6	2	2
5	0	3
5	5	1
4	8	0
4	3	2
3	6	1
3	1	3
2	9	0
2	4	2
1	7	1
1	2	3
0	10	0
0	5	2
0	0	4

MISSION FILE 2:4

Flower power!

TM

1) RRR, RRW, RWW, WWW
(4 solutions)
(NB: RRW = RWR = WRR because they are all two bunches of red and one bunch of white, so these count as just one solution)

2) RRRR, RRRW, RRWW, RWWW, WWWW
(5 solutions)

M1

1) RRRRRRR, RRRRRRW, RRRRRWW, RRRRWWW, RRRWWWW, RRWWWWW, RWWWWWW, WWWWWWW
(8 solutions)

2) RRRRRRRRR, RRRRRRRRW, RRRRRRRWW, RRRRRRRWWW, RRRRRRWWWW, RRRRRWWWWW, RRRRWWWWWW, RRRWWWWWWW, RRWWWWWWWW, RWWWWWWWWW, WWWWWWWWWW

10 bunches have 11 solutions.

Da Vinci files

RRR, RRW, RRB, RWW, RBB, RWB, BBB, BBW, BWW, WWW
(10 combinations)

MISSION FILE 2:5

Legs everywhere!

TM

Officers	8	6	4	2
Dogs	1	2	3	4

M1

1)

Officers	12	10	8	6	4	2
Dogs	1	2	3	4	5	6

2) 4 dogs and 10 Officers

Da Vinci files

Officers	18	16	14	12	10	8	6	4	2
Dogs	1	2	3	4	5	6	7	8	9

MISSION FILE 2:6

Target practice!

TM

1) 3 x 5 = 15
2) 1, 3, 5 or 1, 4, 4 or 2, 3, 4 or 2, 2, 5   – 4 ways

M1

1) 1, 4, 5 or 2, 4, 4 or 2, 3, 5   or 3, 3, 4   – 4 ways
2) 4 x 5 = 20
3) 1, 1, 3, 5   1, 1, 4, 4   1, 2, 2, 5   1, 2, 3, 4   1, 3, 3, 3
    2, 2, 3, 3   2, 2, 2, 4

    7 ways

Da Vinci files

Scores that can be obtained with 3 arrows are:
3, 4, 5, 6, 7, 8, 9, 10, 11, 12, 13, 14, 15

Some of these scores can be obtained in more than one way.

A mountain of a problem

TM

1) 4 jumpers = 5 ways

General	0	1	2	3	4
Ivor	4	3	2	1	0

2) 5 jumpers = 6 ways

General	0	1	2	3	4	5
Ivor	5	4	3	2	1	0

3) 2 jumpers = 3 ways

General	0		1		2	
Ivor	2		1		0	

3 jumpers = 4 ways

General	0	1	2	3
Ivor	3	2	1	0

NB: Children may choose not to record both combinations for a particular split, eg; only one of 1, 3 and 3,1 may be written down. This will affect their table and patterns.

Number of jumpers	2	3	4	5
Ways to share them	3	4	5	6

Pupils should notice that both patterns go up in 1s and that the number of ways to share the jumpers is always one more than how many jumpers there are. Use this knowledge to predict other answers (and then get the children to test them out!).

M1

1)

General	1	2	3	4	5	6	7
Ivor	7	6	5	4	3	2	1

M1

2) 28 ways

General	Ivor	Mouse
6	1	1
5	2	1
5	1	2
4	3	1
4	1	3
4	2	2
3	1	4
3	4	1
3	2	3
3	3	2
4	1	3
4	3	1
4	2	2
3	1	4
3	4	1
3	2	3
3	3	2
2	5	1
2	1	5
2	2	4
2	4	2
2	3	3
1	6	1
1	1	6
1	5	2
1	2	5
1	4	3
1	3	4

Da Vinci files

Ivor	General	Mouse	Goat
5	1	1	1
4	1	1	2
4	1	2	1
4	2	1	1
4	2	1	1
3	2	1	2
3	2	1	2
3	1	2	2

MISSION FILE 2:8
what's the score?

TM

1) A plays B   A plays C   A plays D   B plays C   B plays D   C plays D
6 matches (3 + 2 + 1)
2) 3 x 20 mins = 60mins = 1 hour   So 6 x 20mins = 2 hours

M1

1) (6 solutions)

Team A	0	0	0	1	1	1
Team B	0	1	2	0	1	2

2) (12 solutions)

Team C	0	0	0	0	1	1	1	1	2	2	2	2
Team D	0	1	2	3	0	1	2	3	0	1	2	3

3) (10 solutions)

Team B	0	0	1	1	2	2	3	3	4	4
Team D	0	1	0	1	0	1	0	1	0	1

Da Vinci files

Look at M1. Give each score a value (£3 per goal).
There must be 9 goals scored at half time (£3 x 9 = £27).
Work through the matches for combinations that have 9 goals.

Using the answers to M1 there are 70 possible combinations of scores, for example the three pairs of scores could be (0,1), (0,3), (4,1). In order to ensure all possible combinations are obtained a systematic listing needs to be used.

MISSION FILE 2:9
The great train robbery!

TM

1)

1st carriage	R	R	B	B
2nd carriage	R	B	R	B

(2 x 2 = 4 ways)

2)

1st carriage	R	R	R	B	R	B	B	B
2nd carriage	R	R	B	R	B	R	B	B
3rd carriage	R	B	R	R	B	B	R	B

(2 x 2 x 2 = 8 ways)

1)

1st carriage	R	R	R	R	B	R	R	R	B	B	B	R	B	B	B	B
2nd carriage	R	R	R	B	R	R	B	B	R	R	B	B	R	B	B	B
3rd carriage	R	R	B	R	R	B	R	B	R	B	R	B	B	R	B	B
4th carriage	R	B	R	R	R	B	B	R	B	R	R	B	B	B	R	B

(2 x 2 x 2 x 2 = 16 ways)

2)

1st carriage	R	R	B	B	R	G	G	B	G
2nd carriage	R	B	R	B	G	R	G	G	B

(3 x 3 = 9 ways)

Da Vinci files

There are 3 x 3 x 3 = 27 ways of painting 3 carriages.

MISSION FILE 2:10
A right spotty bunch!

1) 4   2   4
    0   3
    6   1   3

2) Yes

5 solutions. Need to use a systematic method using 1, 2, 3... in turn. Could start by putting 1 in the top left position and working clockwise around the table, then trying a new position and starting again.

```
1 4 5      2 4 4      3 4 3      4 4 2      5 4 1
7   3      6   3      5   3      4   3      3   3
2 6 2      2 5 3      2 4 4      2 3 5      2 2 6
```

Da Vinci files

```
3  5  6  8        3  5  6  8        3  5  6  8        3  5  6  8
18        4        17        4       16        4       15        4
1  7  4  10        2  6  4  10       3  5  3  10       4  4  4  10


3  5  6  8        3  5  6  8        3  5  6  8
14        4        13        4       12        4
5  3  4  10        6  2  4  10       7  1  4  10                (7 possibilities)
```

A peculiar planet

TM

1) 3 Zogs and 2 Zugs
2) 2 Zogs and 3 Zugs   or   5 Zogs and 1 Zug

M1

1) 3 Zogs and 3 Zugs
2) 3 Zogs and 7 Zugs   or   6 Zogs and 3 Zugs

Da Vinci files

(8 solutions)

Zigs (5s)	Zogs (4s)	Zugs (3s)
4	1	1
3	3	0
3	0	4
2	2	3
1	1	6
1	4	2
0	3	5
0	6	1

Tree planting!

TM

1) 12 trees
2) 3 rows

3)

Rows	1	2	3	4	6	8	12	24
Trees	24	12	8	6	4	3	2	1

M1

1) a) 1 on each vertex, 5 between each pair of vertices.
   b) 6 along each side

2) a) 1 on each vertex, 3 between each pair of vertices.
   b) 4 along each side

Da Vinci files

There are 72 possible ways. Each of the following combinations can be permuted in 6 different ways amongst Echo, Summer, and Forrest:

2, 2, 20   2, 4, 18   2, 6, 16   2, 8, 14   2, 10, 12   4, 4, 16
4, 6, 14   4, 8, 12   4, 10, 10   6, 6, 12   6, 8, 10   8, 8, 8

12 x 6 = 72 ways.

Man overboard!

TM

1) and 2)   1,9   2,8   3,7   4,6   5,5   6,4   7,3   8,2   9,1   9 ways

NB: Children may choose not to record both combinations for a particular split, e.g; only one of 1, 9 and 9, 1 may be written down. This is if the boats are considered identical.

M1

1) 3 instructions are needed.

   Four from the 5th boat into the 4th.
   One from the 1st boat into the 3rd.
   Two from the 1st boat into the 3rd.

2) 3, 4, 5, 6, 7

Da Vinci files

2 big boats and 6 small boats   OR   5 big boats and 2 small boats

---

A 'foul' act

TM

1) 9, 8, 7, 6 or 5 bags of turkeys

   $2 + 3 = 5$ $3 + 4 = 7$
   $2 + 4 = 6$ $3 + 5 = 8$
   $2 + 5 = 7$ $4 + 5 = 9$

2) 12, 11, 10 or 9 bags of turkeys

   $2 + 3 + 4 = 9$ $2 + 4 + 5 = 11$
   $2 + 3 + 5 = 10$ $3 + 4 + 5 = 12$

M1

1) 7 and 3 or 5, 3 and 2. Two ways to make 10, so arrested either 2 or 3 agents.
2) 7 and 4 or 5, 4 and 2. Two ways to make 11, so arrested either 2 or 3 agents.
3) 7 and 5 or 7, 2 and 3 or 5, 4 and 3. Three ways to make 12. He must have arrested 3 agents.

Da Vinci files

7, 4 and 2. One way to make 13 so 3 arrests.
7, 5 and 2 or 7, Three and 4 or 5, 4, 2 and 3. Three ways to make 14 so 3 or 4 arrests.
7, 5 and 3. One way to make 15 so 3 arrests
7, 5 and 4 or 7, 5, 3 and 2. Two ways to make 16 so 3 or 4 arrests

Check children are working with the rules established above.

5, 4, 3, 2, 1 BLASTOV!

TM

1) There are 12 possible sums.

2 + 3 = 5	3 + 2 = 5	4 + 2 = 6	2 + 4 = 6
3 + 4 = 7	4 + 3 = 7	2 + 3 + 4 = 9	2 + 4 + 3 = 9
3 + 2 + 4 = 9	3 + 4 + 2 = 9	4 + 2 + 3 = 9	4 + 3 + 2 = 9

2) 4 different totals: 5, 6, 7, 9
3) There are 60 possible sums.

N.B. Some children may not write down both of 2 + 3 = 5 and 3 + 2 = 5 etc, because they appreciate that addition is commutative.

M1

1)

2 + 2 = 4	3 + 2 = 5	4 + 2 = 6	5 + 2 = 7	6 + 2 = 8	8 + 2 = 10
2 + 3 = 5	3 + 3 = 6	4 + 3 = 7	5 + 3 = 8	6 + 3 = 9	8 + 3 = 11
2 + 4 = 6	3 + 4 = 7	4 + 4 = 8	5 + 4 = 9	6 + 4 = 10	8 + 4 = 12
2 + 5 = 7	3 + 5 = 8	4 + 5 = 9	5 + 5 = 10	6 + 5 = 11	8 + 5 = 13
2 + 6 = 8	3 + 6 = 9	4 + 6 = 10	5 + 6 = 11	6 + 6 = 12	8 + 6 = 14
2 + 8 = 10	3 + 8 = 11	4 + 8 = 12	5 + 8 = 13	6 + 8 = 14	8 + 8 = 16

$6 \times 6 = 36$ sums

N.B. Some children may not write down both of 2 + 3 = 5 and 3 + 2 = 5 etc, because they appreciate that addition is commutative.

2) There are 12 different totals: 4, 5, 6, 7, 8, 9, 10, 11, 12, 13, 14, 16.

Da Vinci files

1) For two different numbers there are 72 possible sums. See N.B. in TM as children may also appreciate the multiplication is commutative.

1 x 2 = 2	2 x 1 = 2	9 x 1 = 9
. . .	. . .	. . .
. . .	. . .	. . .
1 x 3 = 3	2 x 3 = 6	9 x 2 = 18
1 x 9 = 9	2 x 9 = 18	9 x 8 = 72

2) For three different numbers there will be 9 x 8 x 7 = 504 sums.
(If commutative property is appreciated then there will be $\frac{504}{6} = 84$ sums)

6

Echo is no birdbrain!

TM

1)

Uni (1)	Bi (2)	Tri (3)	Quad (4)
5	0	0	0
3	1	0	0
1	2	0	0
2	0	1	0
0	1	1	0
1	0	0	1

2) 6 ways

M1

1)

Uni (1)	Bi (2)	Tri (3)	Quad (4)
6	0	0	0
4	1	0	0
3	0	1	0
2	2	0	0
2	0	0	1
1	1	1	0
0	3	0	0
0	1	0	1
0	0	2	0

2) 9 possibilities

Da Vinci files

Uni (1)	Bi (2)	Tri (3)	Quad (4)
7	0	0	0
5	1	0	0
4	0	1	0
3	2	0	0
3	0	0	1
2	1	1	0
1	3	0	0
0	0	1	1
1	0	2	0

A tiRING investigation

TM

The area outside the circles could be counted as a region too. Add 1 to each solution if required for all questions.

1) 2 areas

2) 3 areas

M1

1) 7 areas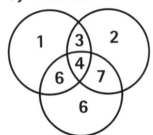

2) 13 areas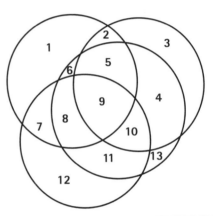

Da Vinci files

£5 x 21 = £105

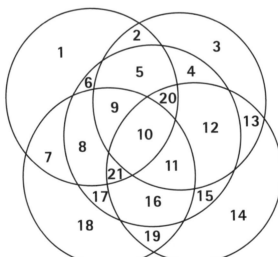

Victor's key to success

TM

1) (1, 2) (1, 3) (1, 4) (1, 5) (1, 6)
(2, 3) (2, 4) (2, 5) (2, 6)
(3, 4) (3, 5) (3, 6)
(4, 5) (4, 6)
(5, 6)

15 ways = 5 + 4 + 3 + 2 + 1

2)

(1, 2, 3) (1, 2, 4) (1, 2, 5) (1, 2, 6)	4
(1, 3, 4) (1, 3, 5) (1, 3, 6)	3
(1, 4, 5) (1, 4, 6)	2
(1, 5, 6)	1
(2, 3, 4) (2, 3, 5) (2, 3, 6)	3
(2, 4, 5) (2, 4, 6)	2
(2, 5, 6)	1
(3. 4, 5) (3, 4, 6)	2
(3,5, 6)	1
(4, 5, 6)	1

(4 + 3 + 2 + 1) + (3 + 2 +1) + (2 + 1) + (1) = 20 ways

TM

3)

(1, 2, 3, 4) (1, 2, 3, 5) (1, 2, 3, 6)	3
(1, 3, 4, 5) (1, 3, 4, 6)	2
(1, 4, 5, 6)	1
(2, 3, 4, 5) (2, 3, 4, 6)	2
(2, 4, 5, 6)	1
(3, 4, 5, 6)	1

(3 + 2 + 1) + (2 + 1) + (1) = 10 ways

M1

1) (1, 2) (1, 3) (1, 4) (1, 5) (1, 6) (1, 7) (1, 8) (1, 9)   8
    (2, 3) (2, 4) (2, 5) (2, 6) (2, 7) (2, 8) (2, 9)   7
    (3, 4) (3, 5) (3, 6) (3, 7) (3, 8) (3, 9)   6
    (4, 5) (4, 6) (4, 7) (4, 8) (4, 9)   5
    (5, 6) (5, 7) (5, 8) (5, 9)   4
    (6, 7) (6, 8) (6, 9)   3
    (7, 8) (7, 9)   2
    (8, 9)   1

    8 + 7 + 6 + 5 + 4 + 3 + 2 + 1 = 36 combinations

2) (1, 2, 3) (1, 2, 4) (1, 2, 5) (1, 2, 6) (1, 2, 7) (1, 2, 8) (1, 2, 9)   7
    (1, 3, 4) (1, 3, 5) (1, 3, 6) (1, 3, 7) (1, 3, 8) (1, 3, 9)   6
    (1, 4, 5) (1, 4, 6) (1, 4, 7) (1, 4, 8) (1, 4, 9)   5
    (1, 5, 6) (1, 5, 7) (1, 5, 8) (1, 5, 9)   4
    (1, 6, 7) (1, 6, 8) (1, 6, 9)   3
    (1, 7, 8) (1, 7, 9)   2
    (1, 8, 9)   1

    (2, 3, 4) (2, 3, 5) (2, 3, 6) (2, 3, 7) (2, 3, 8) (2, 3, 9)   6
    (2, 4, 5) (2, 4, 6) (2, 4, 7) (2, 4, 8) (2, 4, 9)   5
    (2, 5, 6) (2, 5, 7) (2, 5, 8) (2, 5, 9)   4
    (2, 6, 7) (2, 6, 8) (2, 6, 9)   3
    (2, 7, 8) (2, 7, 9)   2
    (2, 8, 9)   1

and so on.

(7 + 6 + 5 + 4 + 3 + 2 + 1) + (6 + 5 + 4 + 3 + 2 + 1) + (5 + 4 + 3 + 2 + 1) + (4 + 3 + 2 + 1) + (3 + 2 + 1) + (2 + 1) + (1) = 84 combinations

OR (7 x 1) + (6 x 2) + (5 x 3) + (4 x 4) + (3 x 5) + (2 x 6) + (1 x 7) = 84

Da Vinci files

6 + 5 + 4 + 3 + 2 + 1 = 21
Which corresponds to 7 buttons.

D.A.F.T. agents get the boot

TIM

1) This could be solved by trial and error or algebraically. If x represents the number of pairs of boots stolen from Apple Farm, then

$x + x + 2x + 2x = 24$

$6x = 24$

$x = 4$

N.B. Children may write a statement in words equivalent to this equation.

Farm	Number of pairs stolen
Apple	4
Plum	4
Cherry	8
Peach	8

2) $6x = 42$

$x = 7$

Farm	Number of pairs stolen
Apple	7
Plum	7
Cherry	14
Peach	14

M1

1) $D = R + 1$

$R = 2 \times M$

$M = N - 4$

From this we can work out Rick = 4

$D + M + N = 13$

$D + M + N + R = 17$

Since Rick is 2 x Mick, then Mick is 2
Dick is one more than Rick which is 5
Nick is 4 more than Mick, which is 6

Check by adding the totals together = 17

2) Could solve this by trial and error. Choose one person for the starting number (it doesn't matter which). Start with this character at 1 and work out the other values. Check the totals. If these are not correct increase the starting value to 2. Continue until the correct total is found.

Mick	Rick = Mick + 1	Vic = Mick + 2	Dick = $\frac{1}{2}$ Vic	Nick = Rick – 3	Total
1	2	3	$1\frac{1}{2}$	–1	–
2	3	4	2	0	11
3	4	5	$2\frac{1}{2}$	1	$15\frac{1}{2}$
4	5	6	3	2	20 ✓

Or solve algebraically:

$N = R - 3$, $R = M + 1$, $V = M + 2$, $D = \frac{1}{2}V$

and $N + R + V + D = 20$

all can be written in terms of M

$N = R - 3 = M + 1 - 3 = M - 2$, $D = \frac{1}{2}V = M + 1$

So $N + R + V + D + M = (M - 2) + (M + 1) + (M + 2) + (\frac{1}{2}M + 1) + M$

$$= 4\frac{1}{2}M + 2$$

$$4\frac{1}{2}M + 2 = 20$$

$$4\frac{1}{2}M = 18$$

$$M = 4$$

Da Vinci files

$\frac{1}{3}$ → Cherry → 2 pairs

$\frac{2}{3}$ → Peach → 2 x 2 = 4 pairs

Apple → 4 + 2 = 6 pairs

Plum → 2 x 6 = 12 pairs

24 pairs in total

MISSION FILE 3:2
what a load of rubbish!

TM

1) List all two digit numbers that are squares and circle the multiples of 12.
16, 25, (36), 49. Answer is 36.

2) List all 12x tables that have 2 digits and circle the multiples of 7.
12, 24, 36, 48, 60, 72, (84), 96. Answer is 84.

M1

1) Summer – between 40 and 70

(Multiples of 7) + 3	(Multiples of 4) + 2
38	42
45	46
52	50
59	54
66	58
	62
	66
	70

The solution for Summer is 66

2) Forest – between 40 and 70

(Multiples of 4) + 2	(Multiples of 5) + 3
42	43
46	48
50	53
54	58
58	63
62	68
66	
70	

The solution for Forest is 58

The winner is Summer!

Da Vinci files

1) Collect 66 + 58 + 44 = 168 pieces of rubbish each day, giving the 1000th piece on Saturday.

2) 6 x 168 = 1008

Hats off to Prince Barrington

TM

1)   To get 24 people:

Families of 3	Gives number of people	Still need this number of people	Families of 4 Needed to reach total
0 x 3	0	24	6 x 4
1 x 3	3	21	Can't do
2 x 3	6	18	Can't do
3 x 3	9	15	Can't do
4 x 3	12	12	3 x 4
5 x 3	15	9	Can't do
6 x 3	18	6	Can't do
7 x 3	21	3	Can't do
8 x 3	24	0	0 x 4

So the possible solutions are:
0 families of three and 6 families of four.
4 families of three and 3 families of four.
8 families of three and 0 families of four.

2)   To get 42 people:

Families of 3	Gives number of people	Still need this number of people	Families of 5 Needed to reach total
0 x 3	0	42	Can't do
1 x 3	3	39	Can't do
2 x 3	6	36	Can't do
3 x 3	9	33	Can't do
4 x 3	12	30	6 x 5
5 x 3	15	27	Can't do
6 x 3	18	24	Can't do
7 x 3	21	21	Can't do
8 x 3	24	18	Can't do
9 x 3	27	15	3 x 5
10 x 3	30	12	Can't do
11 x 3	33	9	Can't do
12 x 3	36	6	Can't do
13 x 3	39	3	Can't do
14 x 3	42	0	0 x 5

So the possible solutions are:
4 families of three and 6 families of five.
9 families of three and 3 families of five.
14 families of three and 0 families of five.

1) 7 stamps at 8p and 7p, total 52p

   By trial and error:

8p stamps	7p stamps	Total
1	6	50p
2	5	51p
3	4	52p

   So three 8p stamps and four 7p stamps.

2) Make 83p

8p stamps	Value Of 8p stamps	Still need this value	7p stamps needed to reach total
0 x 8	0p	83p	Can't do
1 x 8	8p	75p	Can't do
2 x 8	16p	67p	Can't do
3 x 8	24p	59p	Can't do
4 x 8	32p	51p	Can't do
5 x 8	40p	43p	Can't do
6 x 8	48p	35p	5 x 7p
7 x 8	56p	27p	Can't do
8 x 8	64p	19p	Can't do
9 x 8	72p	11p	Can't do
10 x 8	80p	3p	Can't do

So the only solution is six 8p stamps and five 7p stamps, so 11 stamps in total.

Da Vinci files

Possible answers are:

5p stamps	7p stamps	8p stamps
10	2	1
6	6	0

MISSION FILE 3:4
Flying high!

TM

Children will probably work by trial and error.

Each single column can be split into 10 rectangles (4 singles, 3 doubles, 2 triples and 1 quadruple).

There are 6 combinations of columns (3 singles, 2 doubles and 1 triple).

Total number of rectangles = 10 x 6 = 60

M2

1) 10   2) 16

Da Vinci files

Each single column can be split into 15 rectangles
5 single + 4 doubles + 3 trebles + 2 quadruples + 1 quintuple = 15
There are 10 combinations of columns.
4 singles + 3 doubles + 2 trebles + 1 quadruple = 10
15 x 10 = 150

MISSION FILE 3:5
Prince Barrington gets shirty

TM

1)   245, 254, 425, 452, 524, 542
     6 ways
     Could show the children that arranging 3 players is 3 x 2 x 1 = 6

2)   2345   4235
     2354   4253
     2435   4325
     2453   4352
     2534   4523
     2543   4532
     3245   5234
     3254   5243
     3425   5324
     3452   5342
     3524   5423
     3542   5432

     24 ways
     Could show the children that arranging 4 players is 4 x 3 x 2 x 1 = 24

M2

1)   Order for players is: 5   4   2   15   10
2)   10, 5, 4, 5, 10, 4   or
     4, 10, 5, 4, 5, 10

Da Vinci files

2	3 players	10	6 x 6 combinations = 36
10		2	
2		4	
4		2	
4		10	
10		4	

MISSION FILE 3:6
what a cat-astrophe!

TM

1) Use trial and error until the correct total is reached.

FFF	SM = FFF + £1	LFT = FFF x 2	TT = LFT - 4	TOTAL
1	2	2	-2	3
2	3	4	0	9
3	4	6	2	15

So solution is Skimmed Milk costs £4, Low-fat Treats cost £6, Trim Tuna costs £2 and fat-free frisks cost £3.

2) Use trial and error until the correct total is reached.

FFF	SM = FFF + £1	LFT = FFF x 2	TT = LFT - 7	TOTAL
1	2	2	-5	0
2	3	4	-3	6
3	4	6	-1	12
4	5	8	1	18
5	6	10	3	24

So solution is Skimmed Milk costs £6, Low-fat Treats cost £10, Trim Tuna costs £3 and fat-free frisks cost £5.

1)

J	S Given J + S = 5	B Given S + B = 7	T Given B + T = 11	Check T + J = 9
1	4	3	8	9 ✓
2	3	4	7	9 ✓
3	2	5	6	9 ✓
4	1	6	5	9 ✓

Any of these solutions will work.

2)

J	S Given J + S = 10	B Given S + B = 9	T Given B + T = 12	Check T + J = 13
1	9	0	12	The cat can't weigh nothing!!
2	8	1	11	13 ✓
3	7	2	10	13 ✓
4	6	3	9	13 ✓
5	5	4	8	13 ✓
6	4	5	7	13 ✓
7	3	6	6	13 ✓
8	2	7	5	13 ✓
9	1	8	4	13 ✓

Any of these solutions will work.

Da Vinci Files

J	S Given J + S = 7	B Given S + B = 9	T Given B + T = 12	Check T + J = 10
1	6	3	9	10 ✓
2	5	4	8	10 ✓
3	4	5	7	10 ✓
4	3	6	6	10 ✓
5	2	7	5	10 ✓
6	1	8	4	10 ✓

Any of these solutions will work.

Testing times for Year 6 thieves!

TM

	I M Clever	I C Answers	R U Sure	B A Swat
Maggie	X	X	✔	X
Andy	X	✔	X	X
Sally	X	X	X	✔
Dave	✔	X	X	X

M1

	I M Clever / Dave	I C Answers / Andy	R U Sure / Maggie	B A Swat / Sally
White	X	✔	X	X
Green	✔	X	X	X
Black	X	X	X	✔
Brown	X	X	✔	X

Da Vinci files

Three papers numbered 1–8 that total 15. Each paper can only appear once in each combination. The order of the numbers is irrelevant – this concerns permutations.

Paper 1	Paper 2	Paper 3	Total
8	7	6	21
8	7	5	20
8	7	4	19
8	7	3	18
8	7	2	17
8	7	1	16
8	6	5	19
8	6	4	18
8	6	3	17
8	6	2	16
8	6	1	15

Da Vinci files continued

Paper 1	Paper 2	Paper 3	Total
8	5	4	17
8	5	3	16
8	5	2	15
8	5	1	14
8	4	3	15
8	4	2	14
8	4	1	13
8	3	2	13
8	3	1	12
8	2	1	11
7	6	5	18
7	6	4	17
7	6	3	16
7	6	2	15
7	6	1	14
7	5	4	16
7	5	3	15
7	5	2	14
7	5	1	13
7	4	3	14
7	4	2	13
7	4	1	12
7	3	2	12
7	3	1	11
7	2	1	10
6	5	4	15
6	5	3	14
6	5	2	13
6	5	1	12
6	4	3	11

Below this it is safe to assume all the totals are below 15. The 6 possible solutions are highlighted in the table.

Tourist troubles for Tex

TM

1) a) 96 ÷ 4 = 24 people in each bus
    b) 96 ÷ 6 = 16 people in each bus
    c) 96 ÷ 8 = 12 people in each bus

2) 18 x 5 = 90
    so 5 full buses and one more with 6 tourists, so there will be 12 spare seats.

M1

1) 18 + 31 = 49 tourists in all
    wants 23 in rowing boat
          26 in ferry

so 31 – 26 = 5 must move to the rowing boat.

2) $x + x + (x + 1) = 49$ so 16 in ferry / rowing boat
    $3x + 1 = 49$ 17 in dinghy
    $x = 16$

3) 7 left the rowing boat
    10 left the ferry

Da Vinci files

30 tourists, even number in each boat

Boat 1	Boat 2	Boat 3
2	2	26
2	4	24
2	6	22
2	8	20
2	10	18
2	12	16
2	14	14
4	4	22
4	6	20
4	8	18
4	10	16
4	12	14
6	6	18
6	8	16
6	10	14
6	12	12
8	8	14
8	10	12
10	10	10

19 solutions

Victor's in a 'hole' lot of trouble!

TM

1) Start your working from the last day at 0m and add the difference. Check the total at the end.

Day 4	Day 3	Day 2	Day 1	Total
0	2	4	6	12m
1	3	5	7	16m
2	4	6	8	20m

2) Start your working from the last day at 0m and add the difference. Check the total at the end.

Day 4	Day 3	Day 2	Day 1	Total
0	4	8	12	24m
1	5	9	13	28m
2	6	10	14	32m

3) Start your working from the first day at 0m and add the difference. Check the total at the end.

Day 1	Day 2	Day 3	Day 4	Day 5	Total
0	3	6	9	12	30m
1	4	7	10	13	35m

M1

1) Start your working from the last day at 0m and add the difference. Check the total at the end.

Day 4	Day 3	Day 2	Day 1	Total buckets
0	4	8	12	24
1	5	9	13	28
2	6	10	14	32
3	7	11	15	36
4	8	12	16	40
5	9	13	17	44
6	10	14	18	48

Would fill 2 on day 5 (and then day 6 would be −2 so they can't carry on after day 5) Total = 50 buckets

M1

2) Start your working from the last day at 0m and add the difference. Check the total at the end.

Day 6	Day 5	Day 4	Day 3	Day 2	Day 1	Total buckets
0	3	6	9	12	15	45
1	4	7	10	13	16	51
2	5	8	11	14	17	57
3	6	9	12	15	18	63
4	7	10	13	16	19	69
5	8	11	14	17	20	75
6	9	12	15	18	21	81

Would fill 3 on day 7 (and then day 8 would be 0 so they can't carry on after day 7) Total = 84 buckets

Da Vinci Files

	Day 1	Day 2	Day 3	Day 4	Day 5	Day 6	Day 7	Day 8	Total buckets
Doug	28	24	20	16	12	8	4	0	112
Ivor	35	28	21	14	7	0			105

1) Doug fills more buckets
2) 7 more

MISSION FILE 3:10

It's a hat trick!

TM

1) Write out combinations:

BBB
HBB
BHB
BBH
HHB
HBH
BHH
HHH
Giving 8 combinations

Or work through choices

1st man = 2 choices
2nd man = 2 choices
3rd man = 2 choices

Total choices = 2 x 2 x 2
= 8 combinations

TM continued

2) Could also write out the combinations, but by working through the number of choices:

1st man		2nd man		3rd man		Total combinations
3	x	3	x	3	=	27

M1

1) Number of choices is:

1st man		2nd man		3rd man		4th man		Total combinations
2	x	2	x	2	x	2	=	16

2) Number of choice is:

1st man		2nd man		Total combinations
6	x	6	=	36

Da Vinci files

Number of choices is:

1st man		2nd man		3rd man		Total combinations
4	x	4	x	4	=	64

MISSION FILE 3:11
Rubbish engine-eering!

TM

1) By trial and error, working systematically

Carriage 3	Carriage 2 = Carriage 3 – 4	Carriage 1 = Carriage 2 + 1	Total
4	0	1	5
5	1	2	8
6	2	3	11

Could also solve algebraically

2) By trial and error, working systematically

Carriage 1	Carriage 2 = Carriage 1 + 1	Carriage 3 = Carriage 2 + 2	Total
0	1	3	4
1	2	4	7
2	3	5	10
3	4	6	13

M1

By trial and error, working systematically:

Spaceship 4	Spaceship 3 = S4 − 2	Spaceship 2 = S3 x 2	Spaceship 1 = S2 + 2	Total
2	0	0	2	4
3	1	2	4	10
4	2	4	6	16
5	3	6	8	22
6	4	8	10	28

Da Vinci files

By trial and error, working systematically:

Spaceship 4	Spaceship 3 = S4 + 7	Spaceship 2 = 2 x S3	Spaceship 1 = S2 − 2	Total
0	7	14	12	33
1	8	16	14	39
2	9	18	16	45
3	10	20	18	51

MISSION FILE 3:12
Another cat-astrophe

TM

These questions can be solved by trial and error or algebraically.
1) There are 16 people in the room.

$$\tfrac{1}{4}P + 4 = \tfrac{1}{2}P$$
$$P + 16 = 2P$$
$$16 = P$$

2) Three-quarters of the room are drinking tea = 12 people.

$$\tfrac{1}{2}P + 4 = \tfrac{3}{4}P$$
$$2P + 16 = 3P$$
$$16 = P$$

M1

1) 5 dogs and 3 police officers

$$4D + 2P = 26 \qquad \text{and} \qquad D + P = 8$$
$$2D + P = 13$$
$$\rightarrow D = 5, P = 3$$

2) 9 dogs and 4 police officers

$$4D + 2P = 44 \text{ and } D + P = 13$$
$$2D + P = 22$$
$$\rightarrow D = 9, P = 4$$

Da Vinci files

1)

Dogs	Police officers
18	0
17	2
16	4
and so on...	

For every dog lost, 2 Police officers are gained.

2)

Dogs	Police officers
26	0
25	2
24	4
and so on...	

MISSION FILE 3:13

Calculator crazy

TM

1) and 2)   There is more than one way to find all the numbers, so check children's work.

Number to be made	Examples	
1	3 – 2	4 – 3
2	1 + 1	1 x 2
3	3 x 1	2 + 1
4	2 x 2	3 + 1
5	3 + 2	3 + 1 + 1
6	3 x 2	4 + 2
7	3 x 2 + 1	3 + 4
8	4 x 2	4 + 4
9	3 x 3	4 + 4 + 1
10	2 x 4 + 2	4 + 4 + 2
11	2 x 4 + 3	3 + 3 + 3 + 2
12	4 x 3	2 x 4 + 4
13	4 x 3 + 1	4 x 4 – 3
14	4 x 3 + 2	1 + 3 x 3 + 4
15	4 x 4 – 1	3 x 4 + 3
16	4 x 4	3 x 3 + 4 + 3
17	4 x 4 + 1	4 x 3 + 2 + 3
18	4 x 4 + 2	3 x 2 x 3
19	3 x 2 x 3 + 1	4 x 4 + 3
20	4 x 4 + 4	4 x 3 x 2 – 4

M1

Q1 and 2   There may be other solutions so check the children's work.

Number to be made	Examples		
1	3 − 4 ÷ 2 x 1	3 + 2 − 1 x 4	
2	3 x 2 − 4 x1	3 + 1 − 4 ÷ 2	4 + 2 − 3 − 1
3	3 x 2 − 4 + 1	21 ÷ 3 − 4	
4	4 + 3 − 2 − 1	4 ÷ 2 + 3 − 1	
5	4 ÷ 2 + 3 x 1	13 − 4 x 2	
6	4 ÷ 2 + 3 + 1	4 x 3 ÷ 2 x 1	
7	32 ÷ 4 − 1	13 − 4 − 2	
8	4 + 3 + 2 − 1	32 ÷ 4 x 1	
9	4 + 3 + 2 x 1	3 x 2 + 4 − 1	
10	4 + 3 + 2 + 1	3 x 2 + 4 x 1	
11	4 x 3 − 2 + 1	3 x 2 + 4 + 1	
12	4 x 2 + 3 + 1		
13	4 x 3 + 2 − 1	42 ÷ 3 − 1	
14	42 ÷ 3 x 1	21 − 3 − 4	
15	4 x 3 + 2 +1	42 ÷ 3 + 1	
16	34 ÷ 2 − 1		
17	34 ÷ 2 x 1		
18	34 ÷ 2 + 1	41 − 23	
19	23 − 4 x 1		
20	24 − 3 − 1	21 − 4 + 3	

Da Vinci files

There may be other solutions so check the children's work.

Number to be made	Example
21	43 − 21
22	21 + 4 − 3
23	3 x 4 x 2 − 1
24	3 x 4 x 2 x 1
25	3 x 4 x 2 + 1
26	24 + 3− 1
27	32 − 4 − 1
28	4 x 21 ÷ 3
29	32 − 4 + 1
30	13 x 2 + 4

Harvey's having a ball!

TM

1) By trial and error, working systematically:

Number of sausages in a pack	5 packs + 4	3 packs + 16
1	5 + 4 = 9	3 + 16 = 19
2	10 + 4 = 14	6 + 16 = 22
3	15 + 4 = 19	9 + 16 = 25
4	24	28
5	29	31
6	34	34

So there are six sausages in each pack.

Some children may see that unwrapping 2 packs gave 12 extra sausages, so there must be six in a pack.

By algebra, if p is the number of sausages in a pack:
$$5p + 4 = 3p + 16$$
$$5p - 3p = 16 - 4$$
$$2p = 12$$
$$p = 6$$

So 34 sausages.

2)

Number of sausages in a pack	4 packs + 1	3 packs + 10
1	4 + 1 = 5	3 + 10 = 13
2	8 + 1 = 9	6 + 10 = 16
3	12 + 1 = 13	9 + 10 = 19
4	17	22
5	21	25
6	25	28
7	29	31
8	33	34
9	37	37

So there are nine sausages in each pack.

Some pupils may see that unwrapping 1 pack gave 9 extra sausages, so there must be 9 in a pack.

By algebra, if p is the number of sausages in a pack:
$$4p + 1 = 3p + 10$$
$$4p - 3p = 10 - 1$$
$$p = 9$$

So 37 sausages.

M1

1) Two digit numbers with second digit three times bigger than the first:
   13, 26, 39

   26 is the only even one so he must need 26 balloons.

2) Two digit square numbers: 81 is the only possible answer.

3) Two digit prime numbers:
   11, 13, 17, 19, 23, 29, 31, 37, 41, 43, 47, 53, 59, 61, 67, 71, 73, 79,
   83, 89, 91, 97

   Digits have sum of 7 and difference of 5 so the answer is 61 days.

Da Vinci files

28th June

MISSION FILE 3:15

Eggstraordinary!

TM

$4 \times 3 \times 2 \times 1 = 24$ arrangements. So 24 is the maximum.

M1

1) $4 \times 3 = 12$

   There are 4 two-digit multiples of 20 and 3 two-digit multiples of 30, so
   the number of combinations is $4 \times 3 = 12$.

2) $3 \times 2 = 6$

3) $3 \times 3 = 9$

Da Vinci files

1) $13 \times 2 \times 6 = 156$ is the maximum number of attempts.

2) Check children are using the established rules in their investigations.

Best spuddies!

TM

1)

Starter	Main course	Dessert
Soup	Cheesy	Sponge
Soup	Cheesy	Cake
Soup	Cheesy	Banana Split
Soup	Tuna	Sponge
Soup	Tuna	Cake
Soup	Tuna	Banana Split
Soup	Beans	Sponge
Soup	Beans	Cake
Soup	Beans	Banana Split
Skins	Cheesy	Sponge
Skins	Cheesy	Cake
Skins	Cheesy	Banana Split
Skins	Tuna	Sponge
Skins	Tuna	Cake
Skins	Tuna	Banana Split
Skins	Beans	Sponge
Skins	Beans	Cake
Skins	Beans	Banana Split
Pâté	Cheesy	Sponge
Pâté	Cheesy	Cake
Pâté	Cheesy	Banana Split
Pâté	Tuna	Sponge
Pâté	Tuna	Cake
Pâté	Tuna	Banana Split
Pâté	Beans	Sponge
Pâté	Beans	Cake
Pâté	Beans	Banana Split

27 possible combinations

1) By trial and error, use multiples of 50p.
   Can also be solved using algebra:

   $C + T = £3.50$ } → $C - S = £1.50$ } $2C = £6.00$
   $S + T = £2.00$ }   } $C = £3.00$
   $S + C = £4.50$

   So cheese spud = £3.00, tea = 50p and sponge pudding = £1.50

2) By trial and error – use multiples of 50p.
   Can also be solved using algebra:

   $TS + P = £7.50$ } → $TS - CC = £1.50$ } $2TS = £10.00$
   $CC + P = £6.00$ }   } $TS = £5.00$
   $CC + TS = £8.50$

   So tuna spud = £5.00, potato soup = £2.50 and chocolate cake = £3.50

3) By trial and error – use multiples of 50p.
   Can also be solved using algebra:

   $SB + PS = £6.50$
   $OJ + PS = £3.50$ } → $SB + PS = £3.50$ } → $2SB = £10$ → $SB = £5.00$
   $OJ + SB = £7.00$ }

   So spud 'n' beans = £5.00, potato skins = £1.50 and orange juice = £2.00

Da Vinci files

100 potatoes a day for 3 weeks gives $100 \times 21 = 2100$ potatoes.
Sequence 1, 2, 4, 7, 11, 16, 22, 29 ... gives a total of 1561 potatoes.
They should choose the first option, 100 potatoes a day for 3 weeks.

MISSION FILE 3:17
A cracker of a 'case' for Crimes

TM

1) All totals are multiples of 5 so only use those in working out the answer.

H (crates)	R (rucksacks) = 15 − H	C (cases) = 30 − R	Check C + H = 25
5	10	20	YES

TM

2) All totals are multiples of 5 so only use those in working out the answer.

H (crates)	R (rucksacks) = 35 – H	C (cases) = 30 – R	Check C + H = 25
5	30	0	NO
10	25	5	NO
15	20	10	YES

M1

America = 35
Belgium = 15
Canada = 25

Da Vinci files

1) No
2) 252 – 3hrs 8mins = 252 – 188 = 64 minutes

MISSION FILE 3:18

A gem of a crime!

TM

1) 7 ways (assuming vans are identical and at least one agent in a van)
Label the agents A, B, C, D

Van 1	Van 2
AB	CD
AC	BD
AD	BC
ABC	D
ABD	C
ACD	B
BCD	A

2) 6 ways (assuming vans are identical and at least one agent in a van)

Van 1	Van 2	Van 3
AB	C	D
AC	B	D
AD	B	C
BC	A	D
BD	A	C
CD	A	B

M1

8 possible ways

Nick	V T P	V T	V P	T P	V	T	P	–
Rob	–	P	T	V	T P	P V	T V	V T P

Da Vinci files

27 possible ways

Nick	V T P	V T	V T	V P	V P	T P	T P	V	V	V	V	T	T	T	T	P	P	P	P	–	–	–
ROB	–	P	–	T	–	V	–	T P	P	T	–	V P	V	P	–	T V	T	V	–	T V P	T V	T P
Phil	–	–	P	–	T	–	V	–	T	P	T P	–	P	V	P V	–	V	T	T V	–	P	V

Nick	–	–	–	–	–
ROB	P V	T	V	P	–
Phil	T	V P	T P	T V	T V P

A 'daft' potion!

TM

1) 20 g ($\frac{1}{3}$ of 60g)
2) 20 g (same weight as the jam)
3) 10 g (one egg is half the weight of mud/jam)
4) 27.5 g (two sausages are $\frac{1}{4}$ of the weight = 55g, so one sausage is $\frac{1}{2}$ of 55g)
5) 55 g ($\frac{1}{4}$ of the weight)

M1

16 jugs = 18 litres or 18000 ml
1 jug = 1125 ml
1) 4.5 litres or 4500 ml (4 jugs = 4 x 1125 ml)
2) 1.125 litres or 1125 ml
3) 8 jugs (twice the amount)

Da Vinci files

1) 1 litre x 9 bottles = 9 litres, so need 2 jugs of spider spit.
2) 4 litres x 9 bottles = 36 litres, so need 8 jugs of spider spit.

Earth-shattering news for Sandy

TM

This could be solved by trial and improvement, choosing numbers of men and women and checking if they fit the statements. Be careful to take Sam into account.

First engine
2 women and 3 men

Second engine
1 woman and 4 men

M1

Keep working out the groups for one child and check if they satisfy the conditions for the other. Remember to take children themselves into account!

This will probably be solved by trial and improvement, could be solved algebraically.

1)   Solution is 7 boys and 3 girls = 10 children in the Berry family
2)   Solution is 3 boys and 6 girls = 9 children in the Doe family
3)   Solution is 4 boys and 9 girls = 13 children in the Tricky family

Da Vinci files

1) Perry – Zippy   2) Terry – Fluffy   3) Gerry – Beanie   4) Kerry – Pixie

---

MISSION FILE 4:3
Echo shows she has bottle!

TM

1)   54 bottles   (9 x 6)   3)   72 magazines   (8 x 9)
2)   104 cans   (13 x 8)   4)   168 newspapers   (14 x 12)

M1

1)   Start with 1 bottle bin and see if you can complete the length with can bins, then try 2 bottle bins and so on. There are three solutions to choose from.

Bottles (in 6s)	1	2	3	4	5	6	7
Cans (in 4s)	10	Can't do	Can't do	Can't do	4	Can't do	1

2) and 3)

Bottles (in 6s)	1	2	3	4	5	6	7	8	9
Cans (in 4s)	13	Can't do	10	Can't do	7	Can't do	4	Can't do	1

Da Vinci files

The possible solutions are:

Bottles (in 6s)	1	1	1	1	2	2	2	3	3	3
Cans (in 4s)	1	4	7	10	1	4	7	1	4	7
Paper (in 3s)	14	10	6	2	12	8	4	10	6	2

Bottles (in 6s)	4	4	5	5	6	7
Cans (in 4s)	1	4	1	4	1	1
Paper (in 3s)	8	4	6	2	4	2

MISSION FILE 4:4
Cat-astrophe for Echo!

TM

1) One square of 10 x 10, the other of 5 x 5.
2) 10m bars round the outside, 5m bars inside divisors.

M1

1) Small pen 1km x 1km = 1km². Large pen = 11km x 11km = 121km².
2) Two identical rectangles with lengths of 8 km and widths of 4 km to give total 48 km
3)

8 lengths of fence = 6 km each
Length of one edge = 2 km
Perimeter of each small square = 4 x 2 km = 8 km

Da Vinci files

Answers might include square, rectangle, kite, hexagon, quadrilateral, isosceles triangle
– depends on the dimensions of the triangles used.

MISSION FILE 4:5
Eat your greens, Echo!

TM

1) 4 km   (4 + 4 + 8 + 8 = 24)
2) 5 km   (5 + 5 + 10 + 10 = 30)

M1

1) and 2)

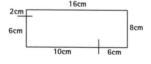
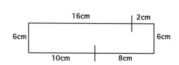

3) Hexagon: e.g.

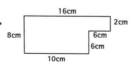

Triangle: e.g.

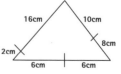

Other shapes may be possible

Da Vinci files

Day	Number of caterpillars	Cabbages eaten	Cabbages left
Start			225
Day 1	3	9	216
Day 2	4	12	204
Day 3	5	15	189
Day 4	6	18	171
Day 5	7	21	150
Day 6	8	24	126
Day 7	9	27	99
Day 8	10	30	69
Day 9	11	33	36
Day 10	12	36	0

Solution = 10 days

MISSION FILE 4:6
A brief challenge for Prince Barrington

TM
80m

M1
1) 11 x 6 km = 66 km
2) 66 ÷ 12 = $5\frac{1}{2}$ hrs or 5 hours and 30 mins
3) 3 hrs + 11 hrs = 14 hrs

Da Vinci files
1) 19 x 10 = 190 km   2) 190 ÷ 9.5 = 20 hrs

MISSION FILE 4:7
Rocket science

TM
1) 35
2) 28
3) 28 (2 + 3 + 5 + 7 + 11)

M1

1) Assuming the mechanics are considered to be identical:

2, 4, 22	2, 6, 20	2, 8, 18	2, 10, 16	2, 12, 14	4, 6, 18
4, 8, 16	4, 10, 14	6, 8, 14	6, 10, 12		

2) Assuming the pensioners are considered to be identical:

1, 3, 33	1, 5, 31	1, 7, 29	1, 9, 27	1, 11, 25	1, 13, 23
1, 15, 21	1, 17, 19	3, 5, 29	3, 7, 27	3, 9, 25	3, 11. 23
3, 13, 21	3, 15, 19	5, 7, 25	5, 9, 23	5, 11, 21	5, 13, 19
5, 15, 17	7, 9, 21	7, 11, 19	7, 13, 17	9, 11, 17	9, 13, 15

Da Vinci files

4 solutions: 2, 2, 2, 24   4, 4, 4, 18   6, 6, 6, 12   8, 8, 8, 6

MISSION FILE 4:8
An Eggs-traordinary challenge for Echo

TM

1) Start at 2 and count up in 3s: (2) 5, 8, 11, 14, 17, 20, 23, 26, 29
Start at 3 and count up in 7s: (3) 10, 17, 24
17 appears on both lists, so 17 birds.

2) Start at 7 and count up in 8s: (7) 15, 23, 31, 39, 47
Start at 2 and count up in 9s: (2) 11, 20, 29, 38, 47
47 appears on both lists, so 47 birds.

M1

1) Start at 6 and count up in 7s: (6) 13, 20, 27, 34, 41, 48, 55, 62, 69, 76, 83, 90, 97
Start at 1 and count up in 4s: (1) 5, 9, 13, 17, 21, 25, 29, 33, 37, 41, 45, 49, 53, 57, 61, 65, 69, 73, 77, 81, 85, 89, 93, 97
13, 41, 69, 97 appear in both lists so they are all possible solutions.

M1

1) Start at 6 and count up in 7s: (6) 13, 20, 27, 34, 41, 48, 55, 62, 69, 76, 83, 90, 97
Start at 1 and count up in 4s: (1) 5, 9, 13, 17, 21, 25, 29, 33, 37, 41, 45, 49, 53, 57, 61, 65, 69, 73, 77, 81, 85, 89, 93, 97
13, 41, 69, 97 appear in both lists so they are all possible solutions.

2) Start at 3 and count in 5s: (3) 8, 13, 18, 23, 28, 33, 38, 43, 48, 53, 58, 63, 68, 73, 78, 83, 88, 93, 98
Start at 1 and count in 3s: (1) 4, 7, 10, 13, 16, 19, 22, 25, 28, 31, 34, 37, 40, 43, 46, 49, 52, 55, 58, 61, 64, 67, 70, 73, 76, 79, 82, 85, 88, 91, 94, 97
13, 28, 43, 58, 73 and 88 appear in both lists so they are all possible solutions.

Da Vinci files

Start at the end and work backwards. Solution is 48 eggs to start with.

It's snow joke!

TM

1)

Main land		Island
1 man stay	2 boys ——————→	
1 man	←—————— 1 boy	1 boy stays
1 boy stays	1 man ——————→	1 boy
1 boy	←—————— 1 boy	1 man stays
	2 boys ——————→	1 man
COMPLETED! ALL AT THE ISLAND		

M1

Main land		Island
1 man and 1 boy stay	2 boys ——————→	
1 man and 1 boy	←—————— 1 boy	1 boy stays
2 boys stay	1 man ——————→	1 boy
2 boys	←—————— 1 boy	1 man stays
1 boy stays	2 boys ——————→	1 man
1 boy	←—————— 1 boy	1 man and 1 boy
	2 boys ——————→	1 man and 1 boy
COMPLETED! ALL AT THE ISLAND		

2)a

Main land		Island
2 men stay	2 boys ——————→	
2 men	←—————— 1 boy	1 boy stays
1 man and 1 boy stay	1 man ——————→	1 boy
1 man and 1 boy	←—————— 1 boy	1 man stays
1 man stays	2 boys ——————→	1 man
1 man	←—————— 1 boy	1 man and 1 boy
1 boy stays	1 man ——————→	1 man and 1 boy
1 boy	←—————— 1 boy	2 men stay
	2 boys ——————→	2 men
COMPLETED! ALL AT THE ISLAND		

2)b 9 trips at 2 hours each = 18 hours

Da Vinci files

1)

Main land		Island Trip 1
1 man stays	2 boys ——————→ 1 man ——————→	
1 man	←—————— 1 boy ←—————— 1 boy	1 man stays
2 boys	1 man ——————→ 1 man ——————→	
COMPLETED! ALL AT THE ISLAND		

2)   Rowing at 20km an hour it will take 3 hours to get to the island.
Total time = 3 journeys x 3 hours = 9 hours

MISSION FILE 4:10
Musical chairs

TM

1) 10 solutions (chairs labelled A – E)
   AB AC AD AE BC BD BE CD CE DE

2) 21 solutions (chairs labelled A – G)
   AB AC AD AE AF AG BC BD BE BF BG CD CE CF CG DE DF DG EF EG FG

M1

1) 15 solutions (chairs labelled A – F)
   AB AC AD AE AF
   BC BD BE BF
   CD CE CF
   DE DF
   EF

M1

2) 20 solutions

ABC	ABD	ABE	ABF	BCD	BCE	BCF	CDE	CDF	DEF
ACD	ACE	ACF		BDE	BDF		CEF		
ADE	ADF			BEF					
AEF									

3) 15 solutions

ABCD	ABCE	ABCF	BCDE	BCDF	CDEF
ABDE	ABDF		BCEF		
ABEF			BDEF		
ACDE	ACDF				
ACEF					
ADEF					

Da Vinci files

Seat 1	Seat 2	Seat 3
Greece	France	GB
USA	Japan	Russia
Seat 4	Seat 5	Seat 6

MISSION FILE 4:11
A cracker of a code

TM

1) $24 + 1 + 4 + 1 + 3 + 6 + 2 + 23 + 7 = 71$
2) $9 + 8 + 26 + 21 + P = 66$ $P = 2$

M1

1) 2 W + 5 + 1 + 5 + 2 + 5 + 17 + 15 = 70   W=10
2) U = 11
3) HI 12321 AM = 80 and HI 41251 AR = 63 + R = 80 − 8 = 72 so R = 72 − 63 = 9

Da Vinci files

1) TX 51322 BC = 51   so 33 + T + X = 51   and   T+ X = 18

Possible Solutions   (Remember T is more than X)

T	17	16	15	14	13	12	11	10	9
X	1	2	3	4	5	6	7	8	9
Possible solution?	No J = 1	No P = 2	No D = 15	Yes	No L = 13	No B = 12	No A = 7	No C = 8	No − T must be greater than X

MISSION FILE 4:12
wire worries for victor

TM

1) 30 cm   2 + 4 + 6 + 8 + 10 = (1 x 2) + (2 x 2) + (3 x 2) + (4 x 2) + (5 x 2)
2) 110 cm   = 2 (1 + 2 + 3 + 4 + 5)
                             = 2 x 15

M1

1) 630 cm   For 3s (1 x 3) + (2 x 3) + (3 x 3) + ... + (20 x 3)
             = 3 x (1 + 2 + 3 +... + 20)
             = 3 x 210
2) 840 cm (4 x 210)
3) 1050 cm   (5 x 210)

Da Vinci files

The rule is length of cut x 210 cm so 90 x 210 = 18900 cm cut

---

MISSION FILE 4:13
A pacey PC!

TM

1) 4 km   2) 6 ways   3) 6 routes

M1

1) 18 km
2) 23
3) 24 km, 30 km, 36 km, 42 km, 48 km, 54 km

Da Vinci files

1) 3 hours 2) 9 km/hr

MISSION FILE 4:14
Sandy gets sandy

TM

1) 24 m   Multiples of 3:   3, 6, 9, 12, 15, 18, 21, 24
           Multiples of 4:   4, 8, 12, 16, 20, 24
           Multiples of 8:   8, 16, 24
2) 8, as 24 is the lowest common multiple in all three times tables.

M1

1) 56 is the lowest common multiple of 8, 7, 4 and 14, so 56 m.
2) 33 slabs (7 + 8 + 14 + 4 = 33)
3) 36 is the lowest common multiple of 9, 6, 12 and 4, so 36 m.
4) 72 m   (2 x 36)

Da Vinci files

1) If the area is 64 m^2 then the side length must be 8m. Work out other side lengths in a similar way, 4 m, 7 m and 6 m.
   The lowest common multiple of 8, 4, 7 and 6 is 168, so 168 m.
2) 115 slabs (21 + 42 + 24 + 28 = 115)

MISSION FILE 4:15
Many D.A.F.T. agents make light work!

TM

1) 3 (1 + 2)   2) 6 (1 + 2 + 3)

M1

1) 10   (1 + 2 + 3 + 4)
2) 15   (1 + 2 + 3 + 4 + 5)
3) 21   (1 + 2 + 3 + 4 + 5 + 6)
4) 28   (1 + 2 + 3 + 4 + 5 + 6 + 7)

Da Vinci files

1) 45 is the total number of handshakes for 10 people.
The difference between the numbers increases by 1.
3 + 3 = 6   6 + 4 = 10   10 + 5 = 15   15 + 6 = 21   21 + 7 = 28   etc

Da Vinci files

2) This is the sequence of triangular numbers. Each number can be drawn as a triangle.

```
                                                    o
                              o                   o o
             o              o o                 o o o
 o          o o            o o o               o o o o
 1           3               6                    10
```

(This pattern could be continued)

MISSION FILE 4:16
Light-fingered light stealers!

TM

1) 6 hours
2) 60 hours   First officer <u>starts</u> work every 4 hours
Second officer <u>starts</u> work every 10 hours
Third officer <u>starts</u> work every 12 hours
Lowest common multiple (LCM) of 4, 10 , 12 = 60

M1

1) 96 hours (LCM of 8, 16, 24 and 32 is 96)
2) Worked (12 + 6 + 4 + 3) 25 shifts (don't count the shifts where they rested!)

Da Vinci files

1) 72 hours
2) Midnight on 4th August

A calculator crisis

TM

1)
$3 - 3 = 0$ $3 - 2 = 1$ $3 + 3 - 4 = 2$ $4 + 2 - 3 = 3$ $2 + 2 = 4$
$2 + 3 = 5$ $3 + 3 = 6$ $4 + 3 = 7$ $4 + 4 = 8$ $4 + 2 + 3 = 9$
$4 + 4 + 2 = 10$

(Other solutions are possible)

2)
$3 - 3 = 0$ $4 - 3 = 1$ $4 + 4 - 3 - 3 = 2$ $3 + 3 - 3 = 3$ $4 + 4 - 4 = 4$
$4 + 4 - 3 = 5$ $3 + 3 = 6$ $3 + 4 = 7$ $4 + 4 = 8$ $3 + 3 + 3 = 9$
$4 + 4 + 4 + 4 - 3 - 3 = 10$

(Other solutions may be possible)

M1

1)   8,7,4,1   8,7,3,2   8,6,5,1   8,6,4,2   8,5,4,3
       7,6,5,2   7,6,4,3   7,4,1,8

2)   8 possibilities

Da Vinci files

	Make 1	Make 2	Make 3	Make 4	Make 5
Use 1	1+1−1	1+1	1+1+1	1+1+1+1	1+1+1+1+1
Use 2	2÷2	2+2−2	2÷2+2	2x2	2x2+2÷2
Use 3	3÷3	3−3÷3	3+3−3	3+3÷3	3+3−3÷3
Use 4	4÷4	4÷4+4÷4	4−4÷4	4+4−4	4+4÷4
Use 5	5÷5	5÷5+5÷5	5−5÷5−5÷5	5−5÷5	5+5−5
Use 6	6÷6	6÷6+6÷6	6÷6+6÷6+6÷6	6−6÷6−6÷6	6−6÷6
Use 7	7÷7	7÷7+7÷7	7÷7+7÷7+7÷7	7−7÷7−7÷7−7÷7	7−7÷7−7÷7
Use 8	8÷8	8÷8+8÷8	8÷8+8÷8+8÷8	8÷8+8÷8+8÷8+8÷8	8−8÷8−8÷8−8÷8
Use 9	9÷9	9÷9+9÷9	9÷9+9÷9+9÷9	9÷9+9÷9+9÷9+9÷9	9−9÷9−9÷9−9÷9−9÷9

	Make 6	Make 7	Make 8	Make 9	Make 10
Use 1	1+1+1+1+1+1	1+1+1+1+1+1+1	1+1+1+1+1+1+1+1	1+1+1+1+1+1+1+1+1	1+1+1+1+1+1+1+1+1+1
Use 2	2x2+2	2x2−2÷2 2x2+2÷2	2x2x2	2x2x2+2÷2	2x2x2+2
Use 3	3+3	3+3+3÷3	3x3−3÷3	3x3	3x3+3÷3
Use 4	4+4÷4+4÷4	4+4−4÷4	4+4	4+4+4÷4	4+4+4÷4+4÷4
Use 5	5+5÷5	5+5÷5+5÷5	5+5−5÷5−5÷5	5+5−5÷5	5+5
Use 6	6+6−6	6+6÷6	6+6÷6+6÷6	6+6÷6+6÷6+6÷6	6+6−6÷6−6÷6
Use 7	7−7÷7	7+7−7	7+7÷7	7+7÷7+7÷7	7+7÷7+7÷7+7÷7
Use 8	8−8÷8−8÷8	8−8÷8	8+8−8	8+8÷8	8+8÷8+8÷8
Use 9	9−9÷9−9÷9−9÷9	9−9÷9−9÷9	9−9÷9	9+9−9	9+9÷9

(Other solutions may be possible)

Da Vinci files

Allow children to explore this open-ended investigation. It is theoretically possible to make all the numbers from 1 to 10 using a single digit and the four operation keys.

MISSION FILE 4:18
A purrrrr-fect cake for James

TM

1)   8 (all of them!)
2)   0
3)   0
4)   0

M1

	27 cubes
1) Icing on three faces	8
2) Icing on two faces	12
3) Icing on one face	6
4) Icing on no faces	1

Some pupils may like to write down general statements.
Icing on three faces is constant – always 8
Icing on two faces is 12 x (number of cubes on one edge – 2)
Icing on one face is 6 x (number of cubes on each edge – 2)^2
Icing on no faces is (the number of cubes on one edge – 2)^3 all cubed

Da Vinci files

	64 cubes 1)	125 cubes 2)
Icing on three faces	8	8
Icing on two faces	24	36
Icing on one face	24	54
Icing on no faces	8	27

MISSION FILE 5:1
A gang of thieves

TM

Start 3rd person from blue in a clockwise direction.

M1

1) Start 4th person from blue in a clockwise direction.
2) Start 11th person from blue in a clockwise direction.
3) Start 5th person from blue in a clockwise direction.
4) Start 13th person from blue in a clockwise direction.

Da Vinci files

1) Start at the 5 o'clock position.
2) One sat on the chair and eleven stood behind (12 in all).
3) Numbers 7, 19, 31, 43, 55, 67, 79, 91, 103, 115, 127, 139

MISSION FILE 5:2
Building blocks

TM

1) 7 ways

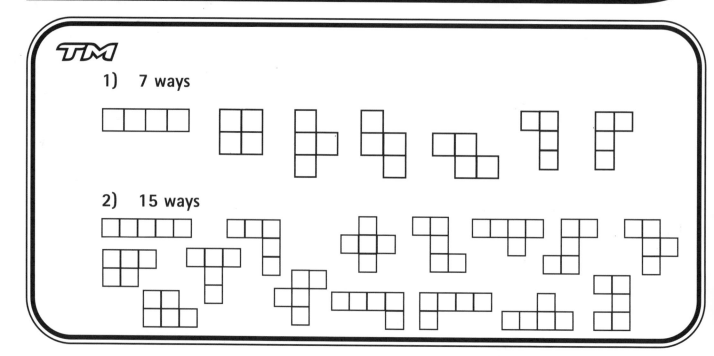

2) 15 ways

M1

1)

Cheapest
2 doors + 6 external walls = £2800 + £9000   = £11 800

2)

Most expensive = 1 door + 9 external walls = £14 900
Saved £14 900 – £11 800 = £3 100

3)

Most expensive = 1 door + 11 external walls = £1 400 + 16 500 = £17 900

4)

Cheapest = 2 doors + 8 external walls = £2 800 + £12 000 = £14 800
Extra spent = £17 900 – £14 800 = £3 100

Da Vinci files

Cheapest = £14 800
Most expensive = £20 900
Difference = £6100

MISSION FILE 5:3
"Cheers, General!"

TM

The weight of the gravy powder is the same as the total weight of the children portions, so $7\frac{1}{2}$ units of weight = 1500 g, 1 unit = 200 g
1)   200 g
2)   600 g
3)   1600 g

M1

12 containers x 180ml = 2160ml   15 jugs = 2160ml   so   1 jug = 144ml

1) 576 ml
2) 72 ml
3) 288 ml
4) 12 jugs (1728 ml) sports energy drink
   12 jugs (1728 ml) fresh spring water
   6 jugs (864 ml) lemonade
   6 jugs (864 ml) apple juice
   6 jugs (864 ml) cod-liver oil mixture
   3 jugs (432 ml) vegetable oil

Da Vinci files

1280 ÷ 4 = 320 ml per jug   Total = 320 x 15 jugs = 4,800 ml

1) 400 ml
2) 640 ml

MISSION FILE 5:3
A [pond] sample question!

TM

1) 1 litre, 3 litre and 6 litre containers
   1 litre = 1 litre   2 = 3 − 1   3 = 3   4 = 3 + 1   5 = 6 − 1   6 = 6
   7 = 6 + 1   8 = 6 + 3 − 1   9 = 6 + 3   10 = 6 + 3 + 1

2) 1 litre, 2 litres and 7 litres
   1 = 1   2 = 2   3 = 2 + 1   4 = 7 − 2 − 1   5 = 7 − 2   6 = 7 − 1
   7 = 7   8 = 7 + 1   9 = 7 + 2   10 = 7 + 2 + 1

M1

1) Fill the three litre container from the pond, fill the one litre container from the three litre so there are two litres left in the three litre container.

   Pond ⟶ 3litres − 1 litre = 2 litres left in 3 litre container

2) Pond ⟶ 5 litres − 3 litres = 2 litres left in 5 litre container
   Throw the contents of the three litre container back in the pond and put the 2 litres from the five litre container into the three litre container.
   Pond ⟶ 5 litre container − 1 litre to fill up the three litre container = 4 litres left in five litre container.

3) Pond ⟶ 7 litres – 5 litre = 2 litres left in 7 litre container
Empty the five litre container back into the pond.
Put the two remaining litres into the 5 litre container.
Pond ⟶ 7 litres – 3 litres to fill the 5 litre container = 4 litres left in 7 litre container.
Empty the five litre container back into the pond.
Put the four remaining litres into the 5 litre container.
Pond ⟶ 7 litres – 1 litre to fill the 5 litre container = 6 litres left in 7 litre container.

4) Pond ⟶ 9 litres – 7 litre = 2 litres left in 9 litre container
Empty the seven litre container back into the pond.
Put the two remaining litres into the 7 litre container.
Pond ⟶ 9 litres – 5 litres to fill the 7 litre container = 4 litres left in 9 litre container.
Empty the seven litre container back into the pond.
Put the four remaining litres into the 7 litre container.
Pond ⟶ 9 litres – 3 litres to fill the 7 litre container = 6 litres left in 9 litre container.
Empty the seven litre container back into the pond.
Put the six remaining litres into the 7 litre container.
Pond ⟶ 9 litres – 1 litre to fill the 7 litre container = 8 litres left in 9 litre container.

Da Vinci files

1) Use the knowledge that $1 cm^3$ = 1 ml.
2) Use the ruler to measure the length, depth and breadth and multiply them together.
3) Find the area of the base (using the formula $\pi r2$) and multiply by the height of the bottle.

MISSION FILE 5:5
A blaze of glory for Sandy's firefighters

TM

1) 1st: Charlotte, 2nd: Maureen, 3rd: Anne, 4th: Jenny
2) 1st: Jones, 2nd: Smith, 3rd: Potts, 4th: Best

Maureen				Sarah				Charlotte				Anne				Jenny			
1st	Best	Knee	RH	1st	Best	Knee	RH	1st	Best	Knee	RH	1st	Best	Knee	RH	1st	Best	Knee	RH
2nd	Green	Back	D	2nd	Green	Back	D	2nd	Green	Back	D	2nd	Green	Back	D	2nd	Green	Back	D
3rd	Potts	Leg	SG	3rd	Potts	Leg	SG	3rd	Potts	Leg	SG	3rd	Potts	Leg	SG	3rd	Potts	Leg	SG
4th	Smith	Ankle	HP	4th	Smith	Ankle	HP	4th	Smith	Ankle	HP	4th	Smith	Ankle	HP	4th	Smith	Ankle	HP
5th	Jones	Foot	B	5th	Jones	Foot	B	5th	Jones	Foot	B	5th	Jones	Foot	B	5th	Jones	Foot	B

Da Vinci files

Change the eight sentences to:

(Maureen) finished behind the lady who hurt her foot.

(Green) did not finish in 4th place

The lady who injured her knee was 3rd to finish and came as Robin Hood.

Sarah Potts came in as an even number and hated dragons.

The lady with the bad back came as a schoolgirl and finished ahead of the lady with the bad knee.

Smith was the second lady to finish and came two places in front of Potts

The person who came in 4th went home with a big bandage on their ankle.

The lady with the hurt foot finished in front of the schoolgirl.

Maureen injured her back.

She finished behind the lady who hurt her leg.

The lady who injured her knee was third to finish and came as Robin Hood.

The lady with the bad back came as a schoolgirl, finished next to Charlotte and finished ahead of the lady with the bad knee.

Smith was the second lady to finish.

Maureen was not married to Mr Best. She was not Harry Potter.

Jones finished in front of the schoolgirl and her bad leg didn't seem to slow her down at all.

MISSION FILE 5:6
A hair-raising problem for Echo

TM

1) 30 blonde, 36 black, 24 brown
2) 50 clown wigs, 125 Rapunzel wigs, 25 judges' wigs

M1

1) $\frac{1}{4} + \frac{2}{3} = \frac{3}{12} + \frac{8}{12} \rightarrow \frac{11}{12}$ so pigs $\rightarrow \frac{1}{12} \rightarrow 12$
So total 144 animals

2) $\frac{3}{5} + \frac{1}{8} = \frac{24}{40} + \frac{5}{40} = \frac{29}{40}$ so goats $\rightarrow \frac{11}{40} \rightarrow 44$ and $\frac{1}{40} \rightarrow 4$
So total animals = 4 × 40 = 160 animals

Da Vinci files

The wording is ambiguous and it may imply that ten kilometres square is a square with sides of 10km giving an area of 10 × 10 = 100km^2.

Ten square kilometres is an area which 10 square kilometres would cover (e.g. a rectangle with sides of 2km and 5km).

MISSION FILE 5:7
Inventions for beginners

TM

1) 45 + (45 + 10) + (45 + 20) + (45 + 30) + (45 + 40) + (45 + 50) + 6 + 0 + 6 + 1 + 6 + 2 + 6 + 3 = 63
2) 10 digits are a 6   (in the numbers 6, 16, 26, 36, 46, 56, 60, 61, 62, 63)

M1

1) 85
2) 30 + 85 = 115
3) 22, in the numbers 4, 14, 24, 34, 40, 41, 42, 43, 44, 45, 46, 47, 48, 49, 54, 64, 74, 84, 94, 104, 114

Da Vinci files

900

A chocolate bar challenge

TM

1) 5 (1 + 4)   2) 20

M1

1) 14 (1 + 4 + 9)
2) 30 (1 + 4 + 9 + 16)
3) The total is always the sum of square numbers.
   For a 7 square the total is $140 = 7^2 + 6^2 + 5^2 + 4^2 + 3^2 + 2^2 + 1^2$

	1 x 1 squares in it	2 x 2 squares in it	3 x 3 squares in it	4 x 4 squares in it	5 x 5 squares in it	6 x 6 squares in it	7 x 7 squares in it	Total squares
1 square	1							1
2 square	4	1						
3 square	9	4	1					
4 square	16	9	4	1				
5 square	25	16	9	4	1			55
6 square	36	25	16	9	4	1		91
7 square	49	36	25	16	9	4	1	140

4) $13^2 = 169$
   13 square contains:
   $169 + 144 + 121 + 100 + 81 + 64 + 49 + 36 + 25 + 16 + 9 + 4 + 1 = 819$

Da Vinci files

	1 x 1 squares in it	2 x 2 squares in it	Total squares
2 x 2 square	4	1	5
2 x 3 rectangle	6	2	8
2 x 4 rectangle	8	3	11
2 x 5 rectangle	10	4	14
2 x 6 rectangle	12	5	17
2 x 7 rectangle	14	6	20

Patterns include single squares increasing in twos, 2 x 2 squares increasing in ones and the total increasing in threes (the two + one).

	1 x 1 squares in it	2 x 2 squares in it	3 x 3 squares in it	Total squares in it
3 x 2 rectangle	6	2	0	8
3 x 3 square	9	4	1	14
3 x 4 rectangle	12	6	2	20
3 x 5 rectangle	15	8	3	26
3 x 6 rectangle	18	10	4	32
3 x 7 rectangle	21	12	5	38

Patterns include single squares increasing in threes, 2 x 2 squares increasing in twos, 3 x 3 squares increasing in ones and the total increasing in sixes (the three + two + one).

Stella hits the jackpot

TM

To discover if a total can be made by a specified number of consecutive numbers, divide the total by the number of consecutive numbers. An odd number of consecutive numbers must divide without a remainder, an even number must end with ☐.5. Once the answer to this division sum is less than half the divisor leave the calculation.

1) 42, 43

2) 85 ÷ 3 = 28.333, so it can not be made with three consecutive numbers
   85 ÷ 4 = 21.25, so it can not be made with four consecutive numbers
   85 ÷ 5 = 17, so the consecutive numbers are 15, 16, 17, 18, 19

3) 84 ÷ 2 = 42, not two consecutives
   84 ÷ 3 = 28, three consecutives are 27, 28, 29
   84 ÷ 4 = 21, not four consecutives
   84 ÷ 5 = 16.8, not five consecutives
   84 ÷ 6 = 14, not six consecutives
   84 ÷ 7 = 12, so seven consecutives are 9, 10, 11, 12, 13, 14, 15
   84 ÷ 8 = 10.5, so eight consecutives are 7, 8, 9, 10, 11, 12, 13, 14
   84 ÷ 9 = 9.333..., not nine consecutives
   84 ÷ 10 = 8.4, not ten consecutives
   84 ÷ 11 = 7.63... not eleven consecutives
   84 ÷ 12 = 7, not twelve consecutives
   84 ÷ 13 = 6.46... which is less than half of 13 so stop investigation here

4) 8

M1

1) Four consecutives are 34, 35, 36, 37
2) Twelve consecutives are 10, 11, 12, 13, 14, 15, 16, 17, 18, 19, 20, 21
3) Eighteen consecutives are 5, 6, 7, 8, 9, 10, 11, 12, 13, 14, 15, 16, 17, 18, 19, 20, 21, 22
4) Two consecutives are 183, 184

Da Vinci files

1) The numbers 1 – 140 added together (i.e. 140 consecutive numbers) total 9870
2) 1 x 2 x 3 x 4 x 5
3) Maximum for 3 digit numbers is 1 – 6 (ie; 6 consecutive numbers)
   1 x 2 x 3 x 4 x 5 x 6 = 720
   Maximum for 4 digit numbers is 1 – 7 (ie; 7 consecutive numbers)
   1 x 2 x 3 x 4 x 5 x 6 x 7 = 5040
   Maximum for 5 digit numbers is 1 – 8 (ie; 8 consecutive numbers)
   1 x 2 x 3 x 4 x 5 x 6 x 7 x 8 = 40320
   Maximum for 3 digit numbers is 1 – 9 (ie; 9 consecutive numbers)
   1 x 2 x 3 x 4 x 5 x 6 x 7 x 8 x 9 = 362880

On your bike, Tex!

TM

1) 8 blips (112, 121, 126, 134, 137, 143, 162, 173)
2) 6 blips (115, 135, 151, 153, 157, 175)

M1

1) Zero
2) 34 ways
   (100, 101, 102, 103, 104, 105, 106, 107, 108, 109, 110, 120, 125, 130, 140, 145, 150, 152, 154, 155, 156, 158, 159, 160, 165, 169, 170, 178, 180, 185, 187, 190, 195, 196)

3) 3-digit blips	4) 4-digit blips	5) 5-digit blips	6-digit blips
0 – 425	0 – 4607	0 –58796	0 – 562374
1 – 111	1 – 1111	1 – 11111	1 - 111111
2 – 317	2 – 6112	2 – 21312	2 - 611211
3 – 311	3 – 3111	3 – 11113	3 - 311111
4 – 981	4 – 3133	4 – 32223	4 - 212233
5 – 531	5 – 5315	5 – 55131	5 - 151531
6 – 681	6 – 2342	6 – 23462	6 - 223221
7 – 711	7 – 1171	7 – 17111	7 - 711111
8 – 617	8 – 3223	8 – 96422	8 - 892348
9 – 331	9 – 3131	9 - 33111	9 - 311311

(There may be alternative answers to these)

Da Vinci files

Consecutive numbers:

3-digits	4-digits	5-digits	6-digits	7-digits
123 = 6	1234 = 8	12345 = 0	123456 = 0	1234567 = 0
234 = 8	2345 = 0	23456 = 0	234567 = 0	2345678 = 0
345 = 0	3456 = 0	34567 = 0	345678 = 0	3456789 = 0
456 = 0	4567 = 0	45678 = 0	456789 = 0	
567 = 0	5678 = 0	56789 = 0		
678 = 0	6789 = 0			
789 = 0				

Consecutive numbers containing the digits 5 or above give blips of zero.

Rows and rows of roses

TM

1) 5 square + 3 square = 25 + 9 = 34
2) 6 square + 6 square = 36 + 36 = 72
3) 10 square + 4 square = 100 + 16 = 116

M1

1)

1 + 4 = 5	1 + 9 = 10	1 + 16 = 17	1 + 25 = 26	1 + 36 = 37	1 + 49 = 100
1 + 64 = 65	1 + 81 = 91	4 + 9 = 13	4 + 16 = 20	4 + 25 = 29	4 + 36 = 40
4 + 49 = 53	4 + 64 = 68	4 + 81 = 85	9 + 16 = 25	9 + 25 = 34	9 + 36 = 45
9 + 49 = 58	9 + 64 = 73	9 + 81 = 90	16 + 25 = 41	16 + 36 = 52	16 + 49 = 65
16 + 64 = 80	16 + 81 = 97	25 + 36 = 61	25 + 49 = 74	25 + 64 = 89	36 + 49 = 85
36 + 64 = 100					

Numbers that can be made are 5, 10, 13, 17, 20, 25, 26, 29, 34, 37, 40, 41, 45, 52, 53, 58, 61, 65, 68, 73, 74, 80, 85, 89, 90, 91, 97, 100.

2) By working systematically, in order, through the possibilities.

Da Vinci files

1+4+9=14	1+4+16=21	1+4+25=30	1+4+36=41	1+4+49=54	1+4+64=69
1+4+81=86	1+9+16=26	1+9+25=35	1+9+36=46	1+9+49=59	1+9+64=74
1+9+81=91	1+16+25=42	1+16+36=53	1+16+49=66	1+16+64=81	1+16+81=98
1+25+36=62	1+25+49=75	1+25+64=90	1+36+49=86	4+9+64=77	4+9+81=94
4+9+16=29	4+9+25=38	4+9+36=49	4+9+49=62	4+25+36=65	4+25+49=78
4+16+25=45	4+16+36=56	4+16+49=69	4+16+64=84	9+16+49=74	9+16+64=89
4+25+64=93	4+36+49=89	9+16+25=50	9+16+36=61	16+25+36=77	16+25+49=90
9+25+36=70	9+25+49=83	9+25+64=98	9+36+49=94		

Numbers that can be made are:
14, 21, 26, 29, 30, 35, 38, 41, 42, 45, 46, 49, 50, 53, 54, 56, 59, 61, 62, 65, 66, 69, 70, 74, 75, 77, 78, 81, 83, 84, 86, 89, 90, 91, 93, 94, 98.

Echo proves she 'nose' best!

TM

1)   120mins = 2 hours

Time	Mrs T and James	Prince B and Echo
40 mins	1 lap	$1\frac{1}{3}$ laps
80 mins	2 laps	$2\frac{2}{3}$ laps
120 mins	3 laps (lapped)	4 laps

2)   2 laps
3)   60mins = 1 hour

M1

1)   4 times
2)   They do 1 lap in 2 hours and travel at 6km per hour
     so track = 2 x 6 km = 12 km.
3)   They do 1 lap of 12 km in $1\frac{1}{2}$ hours so speed = 12 ÷ 1.5 = 8 km per hour

Da Vinci files

Time	Mrs T and James	Prince B and Echo
80 mins	1 lap	$1\frac{1}{4}$ laps
160 mins	2 laps	$2\frac{1}{2}$ laps
240 mins	3 laps	$3\frac{3}{4}$ laps
300 mins	4 laps (lapped)	5 laps

1)   5 laps (Prince Barrington and Echo do $1\frac{1}{4}$ laps in 80 mins)
2)   4 laps
3)   30 laps (24 x 1.25)

No joy for D. A. F. T. joyriders

TM

1)   36 (11, 22, 33, 44, 55, 66, 77, 88, 99 ,101, 111, 121, 131,141, 151, 161, 171, 181, 191, 202, 212, 222, 232, 242, 252, 262, 272, 282, 292, 303, 313, 323, 333, 343, 353, 363)
2)   49 (those in 1) and 373, 383, 393, 404, 414, 424, 434, 444, 454, 464, 474, 484, 494)

M1

1) 25052 − 24942 = 110 miles
2) 25152 − 25052=100 miles, at 60 mph takes 1 hour and 40mins
   From 1pm this takes the time to 2.40pm
3) 4.20pm
4)

25352	25452	25552	25652	25752	25852
25952	26062	26162	26262	26362	26462
26562	26662	26762	26862	26962	27072
27172	27272				

Da Vinci files

10.1.01	10.2.01	10.3.01	10.4.01	10.5.01	10.6.01
10.7.01	10.8.01	10.9.01	10.11.01	20.1.02	20.2.02
20.3.02	20.4.02	20.5.02	20.6.02	20.7.02	20.8.02
20.9.02	20.11.02	30.1.03	30.3.03	30.4.03	30.5.03
30.4.03	30.5.03	30.6.03	30.7.03	30.8.03	30.9.03
30.11.03	11.1.11	11.2.11	11.3.11	11.4.11	11.5.11
11.6.11	11.7.11	11.8.11	11.9.11	11.11.11	21.1.12
21.2.12	21.3.12	21.4.12	21.5.12	21.6.12	21.7.12
21.8.12	21.9.12	21.11.12	31.1.13	31.3.13	31.5.13
31.7.13	31.8.13				

Gives 56 dates.

Dates such as 3.1.13 may have been included. Discuss these with pupils and decide whether these should be counted as palindromic dates or not.

MISSION FILE 5:14
A UFO problem for Victor

TM

1) 6.40am on 2nd May
2) 4am on 13th October

M1

1) 1.40am on 1st January
2) 4am on 5th January
3) Midnight on 5th May
4) Midnight on 27th October
5) Midnight on 29th July

Da Vinci files

Name	Time needed	Time and date have to start
Andy Mann	6000 secs = 100mins	10.20pm on 30th March 2010
Noel Lectric	6000 mins = 100 hours	8pm on 26th March 2010
Lewis Screw	3000 hours = 125 days	Midnight on 25th November 2009
Anne Nail	300 days	Midnight on 3rd June 2009
Ivor Hammer	30 weeks	Midnight on 1st September 2009

MISSION FILE 5:15
A Major dilemma

TM

1) 2.7 x 39.37 = 106.299 inches = (106.299 ÷ 12) feet = 8.85825 feet
2) 6400ml = 6.4 litres = (6.4 ÷ 4.546) gallons = 1.408 gallons (3dp)
3) 3.4 kg = 3400 g = 3400 ÷ 28.35 ounces = 119.93 ounces (2dp)

M1

1) 8 miles = 12.88 km
2) 4 yards = 3.656 metres
3) 3 pints = 1.704 litres
4) 9 inches = 0.2286... metres
5) $12m^2$ = 14.354... yards^2

Da Vinci files

1) 14 gallons x 4.546 = 63.644 litres = 63 644 ml
2) 12 ounces x 28.35 = 340.2 g = 0.3402 kg

Proportions of portions

TM

16 mins $\rightarrow \frac{1}{4}$, so bus $\rightarrow \frac{3}{4} \rightarrow$ 3 x 16 = 48 mins and total = 16 + 48 = 64 mins

$\frac{1}{4} \rightarrow$ 64 mins, so train $\rightarrow \frac{3}{4} \rightarrow$ 64 x 3 = 192 mins and total = 64 + 192 = 256 mins

$\frac{1}{4} \rightarrow$ = 256 mins, so plane $\rightarrow \frac{3}{4} \rightarrow$ 256 x 3 = 768 and total = 256 + 768 = 1024 mins

1) Train = 192 mins = 3 hours 12 mins
2) Plane – bus = 720 mins = 12 hours
3) Total = 1024 mins = 17 hours 4 mins

M1

$\frac{1}{5} \rightarrow$ 20p, so cola $\rightarrow \frac{4}{5}$ = 80p and total is £1

$\frac{1}{5} \rightarrow$ £1, so fruit salad $\rightarrow \frac{4}{5} \rightarrow$ £4 and total is £5

$\frac{1}{5} \rightarrow$ £5, so cheese salad $\rightarrow \frac{4}{5} \rightarrow$ £20 and total is £25

1) Fruit salad = £4
2) Total at start = £25

$\frac{1}{6} \rightarrow$ 30p, so orange juice $\rightarrow \frac{5}{6} \rightarrow$ £1.50 and total is £1.80

$\frac{1}{6} \rightarrow$ £1.80, so garlic bread $\rightarrow \frac{5}{6} \rightarrow$ £9 and total is £10.80

$\frac{1}{6} \rightarrow$ £10.80, so lasagne $\rightarrow \frac{5}{6} \rightarrow$ £54 and total is £64.80

3) Four orange juices cost £6
4) Started with £64.80

Da Vinci Files

Apple juice $\rightarrow \frac{2}{8} \rightarrow$ £1.74, so carrot cake $\rightarrow \frac{6}{8}$ = £5.22 and total = £6.96

£6.96 $\rightarrow$ 25%, so cabbage casserole $\rightarrow$ 75% $\rightarrow$ £20.88 and total is £27.84

$\frac{1}{4} \rightarrow$ £27.84, so sprout surprise $\rightarrow \frac{3}{4} \rightarrow$ £83.52 and total is £111.36

So started with £111.36

Buckett saves the skins of D. A. F. T. agents!

TM

1) 1.25 agents a day x 28 days = 35 agents
2) 200 agents ÷ 1.25 agents a day = 160 days = 22 weeks and 6 days

M1

1) $1\frac{1}{8}$ agents in $1\frac{1}{8}$ days so 1 agent in 1 day
   126 agents in 126 days = 18 weeks
2) 1 year and 20 weeks = 365 days and 140 days = 505 days = 505 agents
3) 504 days

Da Vinci files

1) 32 days → 5 spades, so 64 days → 10 spades
2) $\frac{4}{5}$ day → $\frac{1}{8}$ spade, so 4 days → $\frac{5}{8}$ spade
   8 weeks = 56 days
   56 ÷ 4 = 14, so spades = $\frac{5}{8}$ x 14 = $8\frac{3}{4}$ spades.

8 whole spades of the way to the 9th spade.

An irritating plan

TM

Swimming pool $\rightarrow \frac{5}{8}$ at 1.30 pm

Bingo $\rightarrow \frac{3}{4}$ at 1.50 pm, so 20 mins $\rightarrow \frac{3}{4} - \frac{5}{8} = \frac{6}{8} - \frac{5}{8} = \frac{1}{8}$

1) $\frac{1}{8} \rightarrow 20$ mins, so total time = 8 x 20 mins = 160 mins = 2 hours and 40 mins

2) $\frac{1}{8} \rightarrow 20$ mins and at 1.30 had gone $\frac{5}{8}$

$\frac{5}{8} \rightarrow 100$ mins = 1 hour and 40 mins

1.30pm − 1hour 40 mins = 11.50am

3) $\frac{1}{8} \rightarrow 20$mins and at 1.30 had gone $\frac{5}{8}$

$\frac{3}{8}$ left to go = 60mins = 1 hour

1.30pm + 1hour = 2.30pm

OR − 11.50am + 2 hours and 40 mins = 2.30pm

M1

1) Late

2) 30 minutes late. $\frac{1}{3} \rightarrow 3.07$pm and $\frac{1}{6} \rightarrow 3.17$pm, so $\frac{1}{6}$ = 10 minutes

$\frac{2}{3}$ to go = 4 x 10 minutes = 40 minutes

so time will be 3.17pm + 40 minutes = 3.57pm

The watch is 3 minutes slow making the time 4pm, so they are 30 minutes late.

3) Late

4) 24 minutes

$\frac{1}{5} \rightarrow 11.35$am and $\frac{1}{4}$ = 11.51am, so $\frac{1}{20}$ = 16 minutes

$\frac{1}{4}$ = 5 x 16 minutes = 80 minutes

$\frac{3}{4}$ to go = 3 x 80 minutes = 240 minutes (4 hours)

So time will be 11.51am + 240 minutes = 3.51pm

The watch is 3 minutes slow making the time 3.54pm so 24 mins late.

Da Vinci files

1) Early

2) $\frac{2}{3} \rightarrow 2.08$pm and $\frac{3}{4} \rightarrow 2.17$pm so $\frac{1}{12}$ = 9 minutes

$\frac{1}{4}$ 3 x 9 minutes = 27 minutes to go

So time will be 2.17pm + 27 minutes = 2.44pm

The watch is 3 minutes slow, making the time 2.47pm so, 43 minutes early.

Advancing teaching...
inspiring able learners every day
www.nace.co.uk

NACE exists to support the daily work of teachers providing for pupils of high ability whilst enabling all pupils to flourish. It is an independent charity, founded in 1984.

We promote:
- the fact that able, gifted and talented children and young people have particular educational needs which must be met to realise their potential;
- the use of differentiated educational provision through curriculum enrichment and extension;
- education as an enjoyable, exciting and worthwhile experience for the able, gifted and talented.

We are a large association of professionals offering a wealth of experience in working with more able pupils. We provide advice, training and materials on learning and teaching; leadership and management; whole school improvement to schools and LEAs.
Our publications are the seminal and most comprehensive series of books about able, gifted and talented education.

Our partnership with RISING STARS enables us to provide books which reflect our principles of learning by engaging able pupils in:
- thinking and working creatively to solve practical problems;
- learning from mistakes and seeing themselves in control of their learning;
- working independently and with others;
- expecting to progress to the next level of mastery;
- behaving and thinking as an expert.

NACE membership includes schools, corporate bodies and individuals. Members are teachers, headteachers, school coordinators, LEA advisers and officers, Ofsted Inspectors, psychologists, researchers, HMI, university and college staff, school governors, parents and educators from overseas.

NACE is an independent organisation with regular contacts with national bodies such as the DfES, Ofsted, QCA, ACCAC, TTA, BECTA and the National Academy for Gifted and Talented Youth. Internationally NACE is affiliated to the European Council for High Ability and the World Council for Gifted and Talented Children.

NACE National Office, PO Box 242, Arnolds Way, Oxford, OX2 9FR.
t: 01865 861879 f: 01865 861880 e: info@nace.co.uk www.nace.co.uk
Registered Charity No: 327230

RISING★STARS

Rising Stars UK Ltd, 22 Grafton Street, London W1S 4EX
www.risingstars-uk.com

Published 2004
Reprinted 2005, 2006
Text, design and layout © Rising Stars UK Ltd.

Editorial: Louise Moore, Sally Harbour and Richard Cooper
Design: Branford Graphics
Cover Design: Burville-Riley

British Library Cataloguing in Publication Data.
A CIP record for this book is available from the British Library.

ISBN: 1-904591-88-4

Printed by The Cromwell Press, Trowbridge, Wiltshire